BC SCIENCE 9
Student Workbook

Authors

Briar Ballou
Handsworth Secondary School
North Vancouver, British Columbia

Jon Bocknek
Science Writer
Vallican, British Columbia

Van Chau
Delview Secondary School
Delta, British Columbia

Program Consultants

Sandy Wohl
Hugh Boyd Secondary School
Richmond, British Columbia

Herb Johnston
Faculty of Education
University of British Columbia
Vancouver, British Columbia

 **McGraw-Hill Ryerson**

Toronto   Montréal   Boston   Burr Ridge, IL   Dubuque, IA
Madison, WI   New York   San Francisco   St. Louis   Bangkok   Bogotá
Caracas   Kuala Lumpur   Lisbon   London   Madrid   Mexico City
Milan   New Delhi   Santiago   Seoul   Singapore   Sydney   Taipei

The McGraw·Hill Companies

McGraw-Hill Ryerson

COPIES OF THIS BOOK
MAY BE OBTAINED BY
CONTACTING:

McGraw-Hill Ryerson Ltd.

WEB SITE:
http://www.mcgrawhill.ca

E-MAIL:
orders@mcgrawhill.ca

TOLL-FREE FAX:
1-800-463-5885

TOLL-FREE CALL:
1-800-565-5758

OR BY MAILING YOUR
ORDER TO:
McGraw-Hill Ryerson
Order Department
300 Water Street
Whitby, ON L1N 9B6

Please quote the ISBN and
title when placing your order.

McGraw-Hill Ryerson
BC Science 9 Workbook

ISBN-13: 978-0-07-098467-7

ISBN-10: 0-07-098467-0

http://www.mcgrawhill.ca

13 14 15 16 MP 1 9 8 7 6 5 4

Printed and bound in Canada

PUBLISHER: Keith Owen Richards
DEVELOPMENT HOUSE: Pronk&Associates
DEVELOPMENTAL EDITOR: Tricia Armstrong
MANAGER, EDITORIAL SERVICES: Crystal Shortt
SUPERVISING EDITOR: Shannon Martin
COPY EDITOR: Katherine Hamilton
EDITORIAL ASSISTANT: Michelle Malda
MANAGER, PRODUCTION SERVICES: Yolanda Pigden
PRODUCTION CO-ORDINATOR: Sheryl MacAdam
COVER DESIGN: Valid Layout & Design
ART DIRECTION: Laserwords
ELECTRONIC PAGE MAKE-UP: Laserwords

Contents

Chapter 3   Elements combine to form compounds.

UNIT 2   Reproduction

Chapter 4   The nucleus controls the functions of life.

Chapter 5   Mitosis is the basis of asexual reproduction.

Safety in the Science Classroom

Textbook pages 8–15

Before You Read

Why should you know about safety *before* you start a science activity? Write your ideas on the lines below.

_____

_____

Create a Quiz

After you have read this section, create a five-question quiz based on what you have learned. Trade your quiz with a partner. Answer each other's questions.

What safety rules can protect you and your classmates?

Safety is your first concern when you are doing science activities. You can protect yourself and your classmates by following some important rules.

Rule 1: Listen to your teacher.

 ◆ Listen carefully to all instructions that your teacher gives you, and follow those instructions.

Rule 2: Be alert.

 ◆ Know where the nearest fire alarm is.

 ◆ Know where to find the first aid kit and all other safety equipment.

 ◆ Read the whole activity before you start. If you do not understand something, ask your teacher.

 ◆ Tie back long hair. Do not wear any dangling clothing or jewellery.

 ◆ Wear the protective clothing that your teacher tells you to.

 ◆ Do not chew gum, eat, or drink in your science classroom. Do not taste any substances.

 ◆ Do not smell any substances directly. Hold the container in front of you and waft the fumes toward your nose instead.

Rule 3: Be careful.

◆ Be on the lookout for dangerous behaviour or situations.

◆ Never use broken or chipped glassware.

◆ If any part of your body comes in contact with a dangerous substance, inform your teacher right away as you wash the area with lots of water.

◆ Handle hot objects carefully.

◆ Make sure you know the right way to light and use a Bunsen burner.

◆ Pull on the plug, not the cord, when you unplug electrical equipment.

Rule 4: Clean up.

◆ Clean up any spills according to your teacher's instructions.

◆ Clean and dry equipment before you put it away.

◆ Wash your hands when you are done.

◆ Dispose of materials as instructed by your teacher. ✔

How can safety symbols help you stay safe?

The **Workplace Hazardous Materials Information System (WHMIS)** has eight safety symbols to warn about dangerous materials and products. Look for these symbols on materials and products that you use. ✔

Compressed gas   Flammable and combustible material   Oxidizing material   Poisonous and infectious material causing immediate and serious toxic effects

   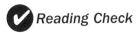

Poisonous material causing other toxic effects   Biohazardous infectious material   Corrosive material   Dangerously reactive material

WHMIS symbols

Reading Check
1. List the four main safety rules.

_____

_____

_____

_____

Reading Check
2. What does WHMIS stand for?

_____

_____

_____

_____

_____

Use with textbook pages 8–15.

What is wrong with this picture?

There are many unsafe situations in the science lab shown below. In the first column of the chart, identify seven unsafe situations. In the second column, describe an injury that might occur as a result of each situation.

Unsafe situation	Possible injury
1.	
2.	
3.	
4.	
5.	
6.	
7.	

Use with textbook pages 8–15.

Safety do's and don'ts

Each of the following situations could happen in a science classroom. Describe the unsafe practices and explain what should be done.

1. You mix two chemicals and notice that a bright yellow gas is produced. You were told to make some observations, so you hold the beaker up close to your face so you can see the gas and smell the fumes.

Unsafe practice: _____

Correct thing to do: _____

2. Your partner's shirt catches on fire while using the Bunsen burner. You tell your partner to stay still while you run to get a cup of water from the sink to put out the fire.

Unsafe practice: _____

Correct thing to do: _____

3. After finishing a lab, you have some chemicals left over. You do not want to waste them, so you carefully pour them back into the container you got them from.

Unsafe practice: _____

Correct thing to do: _____

4. You accidentally spill some water on the classroom floor. You leave it because it is only water and it will quickly evaporate.

Unsafe practice: _____

Correct thing to do: _____

5. You were talking with your partner and did not hear the teacher's instructions on how to do the lab. You figure that it will be okay if you and your partner copy what everybody else is doing.

Unsafe practice: _____

Correct thing to do: _____

6. You need to use some copper (II) sulfate, which is a blue liquid. You go to the shelf and find a flask with blue liquid in it and use that. There is no label on the flask, but it is the only one with a blue liquid in it.

Unsafe practice: _____

Correct thing to do: _____

Use with textbook pages 12–15.

What is WHMIS?

In the second column, write the name of each WHMIS symbol. Then choose the correct meaning of the symbol from the list below. Write the meaning in the third column.

◆ Likely to cause illness or death if ingested or spilled on skin

◆ Will readily burst into flame

◆ May readily react with other substances to produce harmful effects

◆ Will corrode substances with which it comes in contact, including human flesh

WHMIS symbol	Name of the symbol	What the symbol means
1.		
2.		
3.		
4.		

Use with textbook pages 8–15.

Safety in the science classroom

Match each Descriptor on the left with the corresponding WHMIS symbol on the right. Each WHMIS symbol may be used only once.	
Descriptor	**WHMIS symbol**
1. _____ compressed gas	A. (biohazard symbol)
2. _____ corrosive material	
3. _____ oxidizing material	B. (test tube symbol)
4. _____ dangerously reactive material	C. (corrosive symbol)
5. _____ biohazardous infectious material	D. (R symbol)
6. _____ flammable and combustible material	E. (flame symbol)
7. _____ poisonous material causing other toxic effects	F. (flame over circle symbol)
	G. (skull and crossbones symbol)
	H. (T symbol)

8. Which of the following is an unsafe practice in the science lab?

   A. using clean glassware for a lab

   B. using a broken beaker during a lab

   C. using chemicals from a container that is clearly labelled

   D. holding a test tube away from your face when pouring chemicals

9. A student splashed some chemicals into his eyes. Which of the following describes the proper procedure that he should take next?

   A. rub his eyes

   B. stop, drop, and roll

   C. dry his eyes with a paper towel

   D. wash his eyes immediately with water for 15 min

10. Which of the following describes the proper way to smell a substance?

    A. Directly breathe in the fumes for at least 2 min.

    B. Stick your nose in the container and inhale the fumes.

    C. Hold the container at arm's length and waft the fumes toward you.

    D. Hold the container directly under your nose and breathe in the fumes.

11. Which of the following should you do when you are working with an open flame?

I.	tie long hair back
II.	roll up long sleeves
III.	leave the flame unattended

    A. I and II only

    B. I and III only

    C. II and III only

    D. I, II, and III

Section

1.2

Summary

Investigating Matter

Textbook pages 16–27

Before You Read

You can describe matter and how it changes by describing its properties. Colour is one property of matter. Write two more properties of matter on the lines below.

_____

_____

 Mark the Text

In Your Own Words

Highlight the main idea in each paragraph. Stop after each paragraph and put what you just read into your own words.

✔ *Reading Check*

1. What are three properties of matter?

_____

_____

_____

What is matter?

Matter is any substance or any object that has mass and volume. **Mass** is the amount of matter in a substance or an object. **Volume** is the amount of space that a substance or object takes up.

You can describe the mass and volume of matter such as a piece of ice. A small piece of ice might have a mass of 10 g. It might have a volume of 1 cm³. To talk about the piece of ice in more detail, you can describe its other properties. For example, a piece of ice with a mass of 10 g and a volume of 1 cm³ has a density of 10 g/cm³. **Density** is the amount of mass in a certain volume of a substance or object (density equals mass divided by volume).

Other properties of matter include:

◆ **state** (whether something is a solid, a liquid, or a gas)

◆ **conductivity** (how easily something lets electricity or heat move through it)

◆ **boiling point** (the temperature at which a substance changes state from a liquid to a gas)

◆ **melting point** (the temperature at which a substance changes state from a solid to a liquid) ✔

What are pure substances and elements?

Many types of matter are pure substances, which means that they are made up of only one kind of particle. An **element** is a pure substance whose particles cannot be broken down further and still keep their original properties.

How does the kinetic molecular theory describe changes of state?

Kinetic energy is energy of movement. The particles that make up matter have kinetic energy because they are always moving. The kinetic molecular theory states four important things about matter:

1. All matter is made up of tiny particles.

2. There are empty spaces between the particles.

3. Particles of matter are always moving. Particles of a solid are packed so tightly together that they can only vibrate in place. Particles of a liquid are farther apart and can slide past each other. Particles of a gas are very far apart and move around freely and quickly.

4. The more energy the particles have, the faster they can move and the farther apart they can get.

The kinetic molecular theory describes what happens to the particles of matter during a change of state. It also describes how the particles in solids, liquids, and gases are different. ✔

✔ *Reading Check*

2. What is kinetic energy?

_____

_____

_____

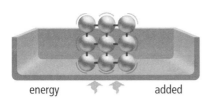

energy   ⬆ ⬆   added

1. Solid gold
Particles are very close to one another, fixed in position, and vibrate.

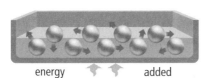

energy   ⬆ ⬆   added

2. Liquid gold
All particles are still close, but now have enough space to slide past one another.

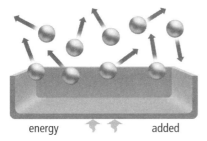

energy   ⬆ ⬆   added

3. Gaseous gold
All particles are highly energetic and move freely to spread out in their container. Further heating gives particles even more kinetic energy, making the gas spread out faster and farther.

Use with textbook pages 16–27.

What is the matter?

Show what you know about states of matter.

1. Complete the following table by describing the three states of matter. The table has been partially completed to help guide you.

state of matter	solid ✓	liquid ✓	gas ✓
shape	fixed shape	takes shape of container ✓	determined by surroundings ✓
volume	definite volume fixed	fixed volume ✓	determined by surrounding ✓
spaces between particles	can only vibrate pact	can move more freely than solids ✓	particles are far apart (lots of space between particles)
movement of particles	particles can only vibrate	slids passed others ✓	moves freely ✓

2. Which row of the table below correctly describes a solid, a liquid, and a gas? _____

	Solid	Liquid	Gas
A.	has definite shape and volume	has definite volume and takes the shape of the container	shape and volume are determined by its surroundings
B.	shape and volume are determined by its surroundings	has definite volume and takes the shape of the container	has definite shape and volume
C.	shape and volume are determined by its surroundings	has definite shape and volume	has definite volume and takes the shape of the container
D.	has definite shape and volume	has definite shape and volume	has definite volume and takes the shape of the container

Use with textbook pages 16–27.

Matter all around us

Vocabulary	
~~boiling point~~	~~mass~~
~~change of state~~	~~matter~~
~~conductivity~~	~~melting point~~
~~density~~	movement
~~elements~~	~~particles~~
~~gas~~	properties
~~heat~~	~~solid~~
~~kinetic~~	states
~~liquid~~	~~volume~~

Use the terms in the vocabulary box to fill in the blanks. Use each term only once. You will not need to use every term.

1. ___Matter___ is anything that has mass and volume. According to the kinetic molecular theory, all matter is made of very small ___particles___ that are constantly moving.

2. ___Mass___ is the amount of matter in an object. The amount of space an object occupies is its ___volume___. The ratio of a material's mass to its volume is its ___density___.

3. There are three ___states___ of matter: solid, liquid and gas. Each of these can change when ___heat___ is added or removed.

4. The temperature at which ice turns to water is the ___melting point___. The temperature at which water turns to water vapour is the ___boiling point___.

5. ___Conductivity___ describes how easily electricity or heat can move through a material.

6. ___kinetic___ energy is the energy of movement.

7. Particles of a ___solid___ are packed so tightly together that they can only vibrate in place. Particles of a ___liquid___ are farther apart and can slide past each other. Particles of a ___gas___ are very far apart and move around freely and quickly.

8. The kinetic molecular theory describes what happens to the particles of matter during a ___Change of state___.

9. Oxygen and gold are examples of ___elements___, which cannot be broken down or separated into simpler substances.

Use with textbook pages 19–20.

Changes of state in gold

Use the graph to help you answer the questions that follow.

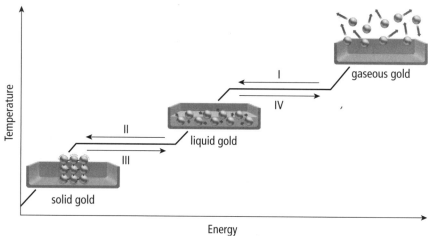

1. What do points **I, II, III,** and **IV** on the graph shown above represent?

   the change of state between solid liquid and gas.

2. What is removed from gaseous gold to cause it to change to a liquid?

   heat energy

3. What change of state occurs at point **I** on the graph?

   gaseous gold to liquid gold (condensation)

4. What change of state occurs at point **II** on the graph?

   solidification

5. What is added to solid gold to cause it to change to a liquid?

   heat energy

6. What happens to the temperature as solid gold turns to a liquid?

   Temp increases no change in temp

7. Describe the change in the kinetic energy as the temperature increases.

   theyr is more kinetic energy added

8. Describe the change in the arrangement of the gold particles as heat energy is added.

   they move farther apart

Use with textbook pages 16–27.

Investigating matter

Match each Term on the left with the best Descriptor on the right. Each Descriptor may be used only once.

Term	Descriptor
1. _D_ volume 2. _A_ density 3. _F_ state 4. _E_ conductivity 5. _C_ element	**A.** amount of mass in a certain volume of a substance **B.** amount of matter in a substance or an object **C.** cannot be broken down into simpler substances **D.** amount of space that a substance or object takes up **E.** measure of how easily electricity or heat can pass through **F.** can be solid, liquid, or gas

Circle the letter of the best answer.

6. Which of the following describes mass?

   A. state of matter

   B. anything with mass and volume

   C. amount of matter in an object

   D. amount of space that an object occupies

7. Which of the following are the main points of the kinetic molecular theory?

I.	Particles are constantly moving.
II.	All matter is made up of very small particles.
III.	There are empty spaces between particles in a substance.

   A. I and II only

   B. I and III only

C. II and III only

D. I, II, and III

8. Which of the following describes what happens when heat is added to a substance?

   A. Particles lose kinetic energy and vibrate faster.

   B. Particles gain kinetic energy and vibrate faster.

   C. Particles gain kinetic energy and vibrate slower.

   D. Particles lose kinetic energy and vibrate slower.

9. Which of the following changes of state require the removal of heat?

I.	melting
II.	boiling

   A. I only

   B. II only

   C. both I and II

   D. neither I nor II

10. Which of the following is the temperature at which a solid changes into a liquid?

   A. boiling point

   B. melting point

   C. both A and B

   D. neither A nor B

11. Which of the following is the temperature at which a liquid changes into a gas?

   A. boiling point

   B. melting point

   C. both A and B

   D. neither A nor B

Atomic Theory

Textbook pages 28–37

Before You Read

What do you remember about atoms from earlier studies? Record your ideas below.

they all have the same mass and volume can't be changed

 Mark the Text

Identify Details

As you read the section, use one colour to highlight the text that explains how the atomic theory was developed. Use another colour to highlight facts about the parts of an atom.

✔ **Reading Check**

1. List three subatomic particles.

_____

_____

_____

What are atoms and how do we know they exist?

An **atom** is the smallest particle of an element that still has the identity and properties of the element. Atoms are made up of **subatomic particles** (particles that are smaller than atoms). These particles are protons, neutrons, and electrons. **Protons** are positively charged subatomic particles. Protons cluster with uncharged subatomic particles called **neutrons**. Protons and neutrons form the central positively charged core, or **nucleus**, of an atom. Fast-moving, negatively charged **electrons** occupy the space that surrounds the nucleus. ✔

How did atomic theory develop?

Our understanding of the atom has come from the work of many men and women in different countries. The following chart mentions some of their most important discoveries.

The theory of the atom	Who developed the theory	The features of the theory	The experimental evidence for the theory
hydrogen atom 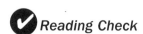 oxygen atom	John Dalton (1766–1844)	• All matter is made of small particles called atoms. • Atoms cannot be created, destroyed, or divided into smaller particles. • All atoms of the same element are identical, but they are different from the atoms of other elements. • Compounds are created when atoms of different elements link together in specific ways.	Dalton used the idea of atoms to help him explain the results of his experiments with compounds such as carbon dioxide, water, and nitrogen oxide.

electrons / positively charged atom	John Joseph (J. J.) Thomson (1856–1940)	• Atoms contain negatively charged particles (later called electrons). • The negatively charged particles are embedded in the atom, which is positively charged.	Thomson observed streams of negatively charged particles while studying electric currents in gas discharge tubes. He inferred that all atoms contained these tiny particles.
electrons move through empty space around nucleus / nucleus made of positively charged protons and neutral neutrons	Ernest Rutherford (1871–1937)	• Most of the atom is empty space. Electrons move in this space. • Most of the mass of the atom is concentrated in a tiny, dense, positively charged central core: the nucleus. • The nucleus contains positively charged particles called protons and particles with no electric charge called neutrons.	Rutherford exposed gold foil to streams of high-speed, positively charged particles called alpha particles. Most of the alpha particles passed through the thin foil, but a small number of alpha particles were deflected as if they had struck something solid. This "something solid" was the atomic nucleus.
electrons / nucleus / energy levels or shells	Niels Bohr (1885–1962)	• Electrons surround the nucleus of the atom in specific energy levels or shells.	Bohr made hydrogen gas glow by passing an electric current through it. He studied the light given off as electrons gain energy and as they give off energy. Bohr proposed that electrons can only exist in specific energy levels or shells around the nucleus.

✔ Reading Check

2. What caused some alpha particles to be deflected in Rutherford's gold foil experiment?

_____

_____

_____

Use with textbook pages 28–33.

Atomic structure

1. Use the vocabulary terms that follow to label the parts of an atom. Place the correct term on the line next to each part of the atom. You will not need to use all the terms.

- atom
- proton
- nucleus
- neutron
- electron
- shell

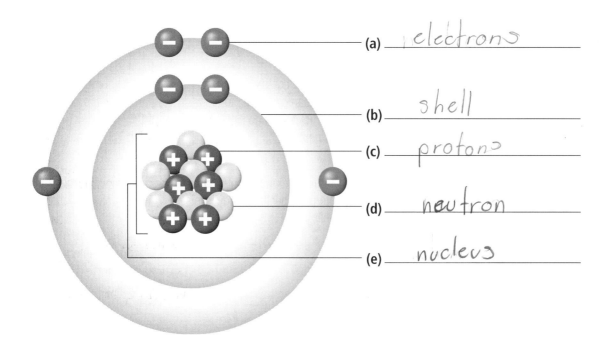

(a) _electrons_

(b) _shell_

(c) _protons_

(d) _neutron_

(e) _nucleus_

2. Complete the following table describing the three subatomic particles.

	Proton	Neutron	Electron
electric charge	positive	Neutral/ no charge	negative
location in the atom	in shell/Neucleus	neucleus	at shell

Use with textbook pages 28–33.

The atom

Vocabulary	
~~Bohr~~	~~neutrons~~
~~Dalton~~	~~positive~~
~~electrons~~	~~protons~~
~~energy~~	~~shells~~
mass	~~subatomic particles~~
negative	~~Rutherford~~
neutral	~~Thomson~~

Use the terms in the vocabulary box to fill in the blanks. You can use each term more than once. You will not need to use every term.

1. _____Dalton_____ suggested that matter is made up of atoms.

2. _____Thomson_____ proposed that atoms contain negatively charged particles later called _____electrons_____.

3. _____Rutheford_____ discovered the nucleus and its subatomic particles. He suggested that the nucleus was made up of positively charged particles called _____protons_____ and particles with no charge called _____neutrons_____.

4. _____Bohr_____ proposed that electrons are located in _____shells_____ around the nucleus.

5. Electrons have different amounts of _____energy_____ and can jump back and forth between the energy levels.

6. All atoms are made up of three _____subatomic particles_____: protons, electrons, and neutrons.

7. Protons have a _____positive_____ charge, electrons have a _____negative_____ charge, and _____neutrons_____ have no electric charge.

8. _____protons_____ and _____neutrons_____ cluster together to form the nucleus of an atom.

Use with textbook pages 28–33.

Contributions to atomic theory

Scientist
Bohr
Dalton
Rutherford
Thomson

Match each scientist to the statements describing his contribution to the atomic theory. Identify who was the first to propose these ideas. Each scientist may be used more than once.

1. Atoms cannot be created, destroyed, or divided into smaller particles.
   Dalton

2. Electrons occupy specific energy levels or shells.
   Bohr

3. Most of the mass of the atom is in the tiny, dense, positively charged nucleus.
   Rutherford

4. Most of the atom is empty space.
   Rutherford

5. All matter is made of small particles called atoms.
   Dalton

6. All atoms of the same element are identical.
   Dalton

7. Atoms contain negatively charged particles.
   J.J. Tomson

8. The nucleus contains positively charged particles called protons and particles with no electric charge called neutrons.
   Rutherford

9. Different elements combine together to form compounds.
   Dalton

10. Electrons move around a central nucleus.
   Rutherford

Use with textbook pages 28–33.

Atomic theory

Match each Descriptor on the left with the corresponding Scientist on the right. Each Scientist may be used more than once.	
Descriptor	**Scientist**
1. _____ discovered the nucleus **2.** _____ suggested that all matter is made of atoms **3.** _____ proposed the "raisin bun" model of the atom **4.** _____ observed streams of negatively charged particles in gas discharge tubes **5.** _____ proposed that electrons exist in energy levels	**A.** Bohr **B.** Dalton **C.** Rutherford **D.** Thomson

Circle the letter of the best answer.

6. Which of the following was not part of Dalton's atomic theory?

  A. All matter is made of small particles called atoms.

  B. Atoms can be created or destroyed.

  C. Atoms of the same element are identical.

  D. Atoms of one element are different from the atoms of other elements.

7. Which of the following was not part of Rutherford's atomic theory?

  A. Most of the mass of the atom is concentrated in electrons.

  B. Most of the atom is empty space.

  C. The nucleus is the tiny, dense, central core of the atom.

  D. The nucleus contains protons and neutrons.

Use the following diagram of an atom to answer questions 8 and 9.

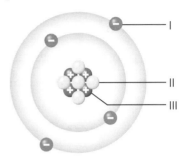

8. Which of the following is the structure labelled II in the diagram?

  A. atom

  B. proton

  C. neutron

  D. electron

9. Which of the following exists in energy levels?

  A. I only

  B. II only

  C. III only

  D. II and III only

10. What is the electrical charge of the nucleus of an atom?

  A. neutral charge

  B. positive charge

  C. negative charge

  D. It depends on the element

11. The nucleus of the atom contains which of the following subatomic particles?

  A. electron

  B. proton and neutron

  C. proton and electron

  D. proton, neutron, and electron

Elements

Textbook pages 42–51

Before You Read

An element is a pure substance that cannot be broken down or separated into anything simpler than it already is. Gold and carbon are examples of elements. What other elements can you name?

Make Flash Cards

For each paragraph, think of a question that might be on a test. Write the question on one side of a flash card. Write the answer on the other side. Quiz yourself until you can answer all the questions.

✔ *Reading Check*

1. List two ways that a metal is different from a non-metal.

✔ *Reading Check*

2. How are the letters for a chemical symbol always written?

What kinds of elements are there?

Most of the elements are either metals or non-metals.

Metals	Non-metals
Elements that are **metals**, such as gold, typically have the following physical properties: ◆ are hard solids at room temperature (except for mercury, which is a liquid) ◆ shiny ◆ malleable ◆ ductile ◆ good conductors of heat and electricity	Elements that are **non-metals**, such as carbon, typically have the following physical properties: ◆ are gases or brittle solids at room temperature (except for bromine, which is a liquid) ◆ not shiny ◆ not malleable ◆ not ductile ◆ not good conductors of heat and electricity ✔

What are chemical symbols?

Each of the elements has a chemical symbol for its name. Some elements have a chemical symbol with just one letter, for example H (hydrogen) and C (carbon).

Other elements have chemical symbols with two letters. The second letter of the chemical symbol sometimes is the next letter in the name of the element, for example Be (beryllium) and Si (silicon). Other times the second letter is from another part of the word, for example Mg (magnesium) and Cl (chlorine).

Sometimes the two letters for an element symbol come from the element's name in another language. For example:

◆ potassium is K (from the Latin *kalium*)

◆ sodium is Na (from Latin *natrium*) ✔

Some Common Elements		
Name of Element	**Symbol**	**Origin of Element's Symbol**
Gases at room temperature		
hydrogen	H	*Hydros genes* = water forming
helium	He	*Helios* = sun
neon	Ne	*Neon* = new
nitrogen	N	*Nitron* = saltpetre (an explosive)
oxygen	O	*Oxys genes* = acid forming
fluorine	F	*Fluere* = Latin for flowing
chlorine	Cl	*Chloros* from *khloros* = pale green
Liquids at room temperature		
bromine	Br	*Bromos* = smelly
mercury	Hg	*Hydrargyrum* = Latin for liquid silver
Solids at room temperature		
lithium	Li	*Lithos* = stone
sodium	Na	*Natrium* = Latin for sodium
potassium	K	*Kalium* = Latin for potash
rubidium	Rb	*Rubidus* = Latin for red
cesium	Cs	*Caesius* = Latin for bluish-grey
beryllium	Be	*Beryllos* = emerald
magnesium	Mg	*Magnesia alba* = a place in Greece
calcium	Ca	*Calx* = Latin for limestone
strontium	Sr	*Strontian* = a village in Scotland
barium	Ba	*Barys* = heavy
titanium	Ti	*Titans* = gods from Greek mythology
chromium	Cr	*Chroma* = colour
manganese	Mn	*Magnesia negra* = Latin for black magnesium
iron	Fe	*Ferrum* = Latin for iron
cobalt	Co	*Cobald* from *kobold* = German for goblin
nickel	Ni	*kupfer Nickel* = German for devil's copper
copper	Cu	*Cuprum* = Latin for Cyprian
zinc	Zn	*Zink* = German for zinc
silver	Ag	*Argentum* = Latin for silver
gold	Au	*Aurum* = Latin for gold
tin	Sn	*Stannum* = Latin for tin
lead	Pb	*Plumbum* = Latin for lead
carbon	C	*Carbo* = Latin for coal
phosphorus	P	*Phosphoros* = bringer of light
sulphur	S	*Sulphurium* = Latin for sulphur
iodine	I	*Iodes* = violet

Use with textbook pages 43–44.

Element names

1. Identify the element based on the clues given. The first one is done to help guide you.

	General clue	Element
(a)	policeman	copper
(b)	to press clothes	iron
(c)	planet closest to the Sun	Mercury
(d)	5 cents	nickel
(e)	to be shown the way	plumbum (lead

2. What is the English name for each of these Latin names of elements?

(a) plumbum _to lead_   (e) natrium _sodium_

(b) ferrum _iron_   (f) kalium _potash_

(c) argentum _god silver_   (g) fluere _flowing_

(d) carbo _coal_   (h) hydrargyrum _liquid silver_

3. Which elements' names have the following meanings?

(a) bringer of light _Phosphorus_ ✓   (e) emerald _beryllium_

(b) stone _lithium_ ✓   (f) heavy _barium_

(c) violet _iodine_ ✓   (g) sun _hilium_

(d) colour _chromium_ ✓   (g) smelly _bromie_

Use with textbook pages 43–44.

Learning chemical symbols

Write the element name in the blank beside its symbol.

1. Symbols that come from the first letter of the element's name

   (a) P _hosphorus_   (d) I _odIne_

   (b) S _ulphur_   (e) F _luorine_

   (c) O _xygen_   (f) N _itrogen_

2. Symbols that come from the first two letters of the element's name

   (a) He _lium_   (c) Be _ryllium_

   (b) Li _thium_   (d) Ne _on_

3. Symbols that come from the first letter and another letter in the name

   (a) Cl _Chlorine_   (c) Zn _Zinc_

   (b) Mg _Magnesium_   (d) Mn _Mangnese_

4. Symbols that come from the name of the element in Latin

   (a) Pb _Plombum_   (e) Cu _prum_

   (b) Au _rum_   (f) Fe _rrum Iron_

   (c) Ag _Argentun_   (g) Na _trium_

   (d) Sn _Stannum tin_   (h) Rb _Rubidus_

5. Use the chemical symbols to write three English words. An example is provided for you.

English word	Symbols	Names of elements used
none	N-O-Ne	nitrogen-oxygen-neon
stone	Li	lithium
titans	Ti	titanium
liquid silver	Hg	mercury

Use with textbook pages 43–44.

Elements in Earth's crust

The following pie charts show the most abundant elements (by mass) in the whole Earth and in Earth's crust (the surface layer of Earth).

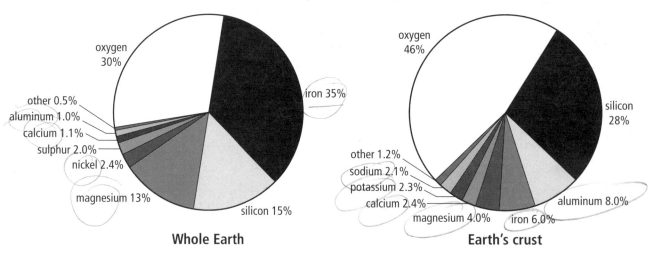

Whole Earth   Earth's crust

1. Use the information in the pie charts to help you complete the following table.

	Most common element	**Second most common element**	**Third most common element**
in the whole Earth	iron ✓	oxygen ✓	silicon ✓
in Earth's crust	oxygen ✓	silicon ✓	aluminum ✓

2. Aluminum, calcium, nickel, magnesium, iron, sodium, and potassium are all metals.

(a) Approximately what percentage of the whole Earth is made of metals?

52.5%

(b) Approximately what percentage of Earth's crust is made of metals?

24.8%

Use with textbook pages 42–47.

Elements

Match the Element on the left with the corresponding Symbol on the right. Each Symbol may be used only once.	
Element	**Symbol**
1. _Ca_ calcium	**A.** C
2. _C_ carbon	**B.** Ca
3. _Cl_ chlorine	**C.** Ch
4. _K_ potassium	**D.** Cl
5. _P_ phosphorus	**E.** K
6. _S_ sulphur	**F.** Na
7. _Na_ sodium	**G.** P
	H. Ph
	I. Po
	J. S
	K. So
	L. Su

Circle the letter of the best answer.

8. Which of the following are rules for writing a chemical symbol?

I.	first letter must be capitalized
II.	symbol is made of either one or two letters
III.	second letter, if present, must be lower case

A. I and II only

B. I and III only

C. II and III only

D. I, II, and III

9. What is the chemical symbol for helium?

A. H

B. He

C. HI

D. Hi

10. Which of the following correctly matches the name of the element with the chemical symbol?

A. magnesium=Mg

B. aluminum=A

C. oxygen=Ox

D. nitrogen=Ni

11. Which of the following is a gas at room temperature?

A. calcium

B. carbon

C. chlorine

D. copper

12. Which of the following metals is a liquid at room temperature?

A. silver

B. sodium

C. mercury

D. manganese

13. Which of the following are physical properties of metals?

I.	ductile
II.	malleable
III.	good conductors of heat and electricity

A. I and II only

B. I and III only

C. II and III only

D. I, II, and III

The Periodic Table and Chemical Properties

Textbook pages 52–63

Before You Read

Imagine you had to classify all of the different elements. How would you organize them? How might properties help you decide? Write your thoughts below.

 **Mark the Text**

Identify Details

As you skim the section, use one colour to highlight the text or labels that talk about the periodic table. Use another colour to highlight facts about atomic number and other facts about each element.

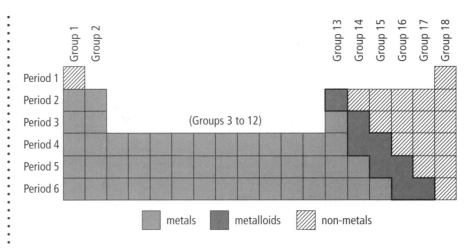

metals   metalloids   non-metals

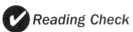 **Reading Check**

1. What five facts about an element can you find in the periodic table?

What is the periodic table?

The **periodic table** places each element on a chart based on its chemical and physical properties. Each box of the periodic table lists information about the atoms that make up an element. You can see:

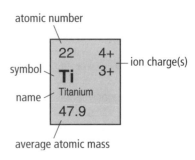

◆ the name of the element

◆ the chemical symbol of the element

◆ the **atomic number** of the element—the number of protons in the nucleus of each one of its atoms

◆ the **average atomic mass** of the element—the weighted average of the masses of the atoms of an element

◆ the ion charge (or charges) of the element—the electric charge of its atoms when they gain or lose electrons. If the atoms can gain or lose electrons in more than one way, they will have a **multiple ion charge.** ✔

What patterns does the periodic table show?

One pattern in the periodic table is that elements are of three major types. Metals are on the left side of the periodic table. Non-metals are on the right side. A small number of elements, such as boron (B) and silicon (Si) are metalloids. **Metalloids** have some properties that are like those of metals and other properties that are like those of non-metals. Metalloids form a zigzag staircase toward the right side of the periodic table.

Another pattern in the periodic table is that elements in a group (vertical column) have similar properties. Because they have properties in common, the elements in a group are often called a **chemical family**. ✔

Reading Check

2. What is a chemical family?

_____

_____

_____

_____

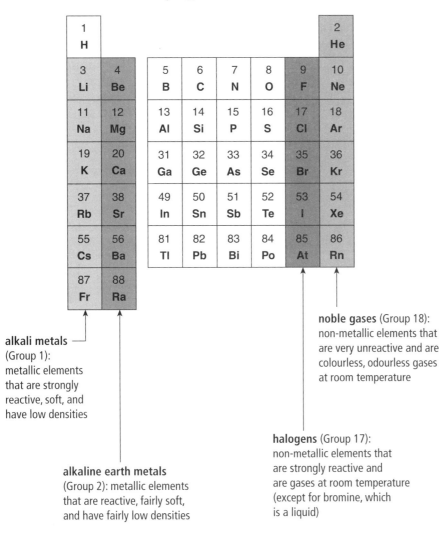

alkali metals (Group 1): metallic elements that are strongly reactive, soft, and have low densities

alkaline earth metals (Group 2): metallic elements that are reactive, fairly soft, and have fairly low densities

noble gases (Group 18): non-metallic elements that are very unreactive and are colourless, odourless gases at room temperature

halogens (Group 17): non-metallic elements that are strongly reactive and are gases at room temperature (except for bromine, which is a liquid)

A complete periodic table is shown on page 202.

Use with textbook pages 52–57.

What is in the box?

Test your knowledge how information is displayed for each element in the periodic table.

1. Use the vocabulary words listed to label the diagram.

Vocabulary	
ion charge	~~name~~
atomic number	~~symbol~~
~~average atomic mass~~	

(a) _atomic number_ → 22   4+
(b) _symbol_ → **Ti**   3+
(c) _name_ → Titanium
(d) _atomic mass_ → 47.9
(e) _ion charge_

Examine the periodic table entry for each of the following elements and complete the blanks below.

2.
| 12   2+ |
| **Mg** |
| Magnesium |
| 24.3 |

(a) atomic number _12_
(b) average atomic mass _24.3_
(c) ion charge _2+_
(d) number of protons _12_

3.
| 19   + |
| **K** |
| Potassium |
| 39.1 |

(a) name of element _potassium_
(b) ion charge _+_
(c) number of protons _19_
(d) average atomic mass _39.1_

4.
| 8   2– |
| **O** |
| Oxygen |
| 16.0 |

(a) atomic number _8_
(b) average atomic mass _16.0_
(c) ion charge _2–_
(d) symbol of element _O_

5.
| 15   3– |
| **P** |
| Phosphorus |
| 31.0 |

(a) name of element _Phosphorus_
(b) average atomic mass _31.0_
(c) ion charge _3–_
(d) number of protons _15_

Use with textbook pages 52–57.

Families of elements

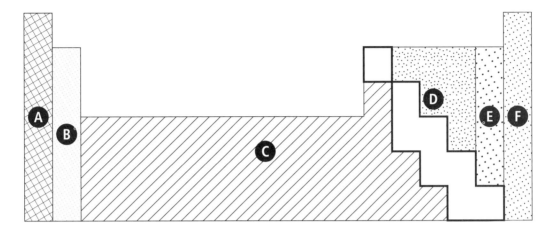

Use the simplified periodic table shown above to answer questions 1 to 12. To which region does each element or family belong? Place the letter corresponding to the shaded region on the blank line. You can use regions more than once.

You can use the periodic table on page 201 to help you answer these questions.

1. helium _____

2. lithium _____

3. fluorine _____

4. beryllium _____

5. halogens _____

6. noble gases _____

7. alkali metals _____

8. alkaline earth metals _____

9. non-metallic elements that are strongly reactive _____

10. metallic elements that are strongly reactive _____

11. metallic elements that are reactive _____

12. non-metallic elements that are very unreactive _____

Use with textbook pages 52–57.

Using the periodic table

Vocabulary	
average atomic mass	metalloids
atomic number	multiple ion charge
electrons	noble gases
families	non-metals
good	periodic table
halogens	periods
ions	poor
ion charge	properties
metals	

Use the terms in the vocabulary box to fill in the blanks. You can use each term more than once. You will not need to use every term.

1. The ___*families*___ organizes the elements according to their physical and chemical ___*properties*___.

2. The periodic table is divided into seven horizontal rows called ___*periods*___ and 18 vertical columns called ___*families*___.

3. ___*metals*___ appear on the left side of the periodic table. These elements are ___*good*___ conductors of heat and electricity.

4. ___*Halogens*___ appear on the right side of the periodic table. These elements are ___*poor*___ conductors of heat and electricity.

5. The ___*metalloids*___ form a zigzag staircase arrangement on the periodic table. These elements have properties similar to both ___*metals*___ and ___*non metals*___.

6. The ___*atomic number*___ refers to the number of protons that an atom has in the nucleus.

7. The _____ is the weighted average of the masses of the atoms of an element.

8. A(n) _____ is an electric charge that forms on an atom when it gains or loses electrons.

9. Some metals, like platinum and cobalt, form _____ in more than one way. In other words, they have a(n) _____.

Use with textbook pages 52–57.

The periodic table and chemical properties

Match each Term on the left with the best Descriptor on the right. Each Descriptor may be used only once.	
Term	**Descriptor**
1. _B_ halogens	**A.** most reactive metals
2. _D_ noble gases	**B.** most reactive non-metals
3. _A_ alkali metals	**C.** have properties of both metals and non-metals
4. _E_ alkaline earth metals	**D.** most unreactive elements
	E. includes beryllium and magnesium

Circle the letter of the best answer.

5. What is the name of a horizontal row in the periodic table?

   A. column

   B. family

   C. period

   D. group

6. Which of the following are metalloids?

I.	silicon
II.	boron
III.	neon

   A. I and II only

   B. I and III only

   C. II and III only

   D. I, II, and III

Use the following diagram to answer questions 7 and 8.

30	2+
Zn	
Zinc	
65.4	

7. What does the "30" refer to?

   A. ion charge

   B. average atomic mass

   C. atomic number

   D. family number

8. What does the "2+" refer to?

   A. ion charge

   B. average atomic mass

   C. atomic number

   D. family number

9. To which of the following groups does oxygen belong?

   A. gas

   B. metal

   C. metalloid

   D. non-metal

10. Which of the following is the same as the atomic number of an element?

   A. number of protons

   B. number of neutrons

   C. number of electrons

   D. number of ion charges

$\frac{10}{10}$

The Periodic Table and Atomic Theory

Textbook pages 64–71

Before You Read

Why do elements in the same family have similar properties? Give your ideas on the lines below.

_____

_____

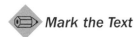
Mark the Text

Check for Understanding

As you read this section, stop and read again any parts you do not understand. Highlight all the sentences that help you get a better understanding.

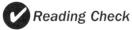 **Reading Check**

1. What does a Bohr model show?

_____

_____

_____

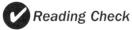 **Reading Check**

2. What are valence electrons?

_____

_____

_____

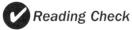

What is a Bohr model?

A **Bohr model** is a diagram that shows the number of electrons in each of the energy levels around an atom. These regions also may be called **electron shells**. ✔

Each electron shell can hold only a certain number of electrons. The first electron shell can hold a maximum of two electrons. The second electron shell can hold a maximum of eight electrons. The third electron shell can hold a maximum of eight electrons.

The electron shell that holds the outermost electrons—the electrons that are farthest away from the nucleus—is called the **valence shell**. Electrons in the valence shell are called **valence electrons**. ✔

Why are noble gas elements stable?

Atoms of noble gas elements (Group 18) have filled valence shells. They hold the maximum number of electrons that they can. These elements usually do not gain electrons, and they usually do not lose electrons. This arrangement makes these atoms very stable.

What are some patterns that involve valence electrons?

Some patterns of valence electrons	Example
Elements in the same family have the same number of valence electrons.	All the alkali metals (Group 1) have one valence electron. All the halogens (Group 17) have seven valence electrons. All the noble gases except helium have eight valence electrons.
Elements that are in the same period have their valence electrons in the same shell.	Elements in Period 2 have their valence electrons in the second shell. Elements in Period 3 have their valence electrons in the third shell.
The period number of an element = the number of occupied energy shells of its atoms.	Elements in Period 2 have two occupied energy shells. Elements in Period 3 have three occupied shells.

How do atoms form ions?

An ion is an atom with an electric charge because it has gained or lost electrons. An ion has a negative charge when it has more electrons than protons. An ion has a positive charge when it has more protons than electrons.

Atoms tend to gain or lose electrons from their valence shells. Use the Bohr models of the elements to help you understand the next three points.

◆ Metals tend to lose electrons and form positive ions.

◆ Non-metals (except for noble gases) tend to gain electrons and form negative ions.

◆ Ions have an arrangement of electrons that is like the arrangement of electrons in the nearest noble gas.

You show the charge on an ion with a superscript $^+$ or $^-$ sign to the right of the element symbol. For example, a lithium ion is Li^+. A chlorine ion is Cl^-.

The charge on an ion is equal to the sum of the charges on its protons and electrons. For instance, the lithium ion has three protons and two electrons. It has a charge of "plus one" because (3+) protons + (2–) electrons = 1+.

Use with textbook pages 64–67.

The number game with atoms and ions

1. Complete the following sentences using the terms in parentheses.

(a) The atomic ___number___ (number/mass) of an element is the same as the number of protons in the nucleus of an atom.

(b) An ___ion___ (atom/ion) of an element has the same number of protons as electrons.

(c) A positively charged ion has ___gained___ (lost/gained) electrons.

(d) A negatively charged ion has ___lost___ (lost/gained) electrons.

2. Complete the following table. Some answers are provided to help guide you. You can refer to the Bohr model chart on page 32 and the periodic table on page 202.

Element name	Atomic number	Ion charge	Atom or ion?	Number of protons	Number of electrons
beryllium	4	2+	ion	4	2
sodium	11	0	atom	11	
argon	18	0	atom	18	18
chlorine	17	0		17	
Nitrogen	7	3–		7	10
calcium	20	0		20	
Sulpher	16	2–		16	
Lithiom	3	+			
Aluminum	13	3+		13	

Use with textbook pages 64–67.

Drawing Bohr model diagrams

1. Refer to the Bohr model chart on page 32 to help you complete the following table. Some answers are provided for you. (Hint: Remember that the maximum number of electrons in the first three shells is 2, 8, and 8.)

Atom/ion	Atomic number	Number of protons	Number of electrons	Number of electron shells
neon atom	10	10	10	2
fluorine atom	9	9	9	2
fluorine ion	9	9	10	2
sodium atom	11	11	11	2
sodium ion	11	10	10	2
argon atom	18	18	18	3
chlorine atom	17	17	17	3
chlorine ion	17	17	18	3
potassium atom	19	19	19	4
potassium ion	19	19	18	3

2. Use the table above to draw the Bohr model diagram for the following atoms and ions.

Argon atom	Chlorine atom	Chlorine ion	Potassium atom	Potassium ion

3. What do you notice about the arrangement of electrons in the Bohr model of a neon atom, fluorine ion, and a magnesium ion?

   They all have 10 electrons

4. What would you expect to see with the arrangement of electrons in the Bohr model of an argon atom, chlorine ion, and a potassium ion?

   that they all have the same amount of electrons

Use with textbook pages 64–67.

Analyzing Bohr model diagrams

Fill in the blanks beside each Bohr model diagram. The first one has been partially completed to help guide you.

1.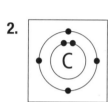

   (a) number of protons _____7_____

   (b) number of shells _____2_____

   (c) number of electrons _____7_____

   (d) number of valence electrons _____5_____

   (e) Bohr model of _____ **a nitrogen atom**

2.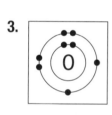

   (a) number of protons _____6_____

   (b) number of shells _____2_____

   (c) number of electrons _____6_____

   (d) number of valence electrons _____4_____

   (e) Bohr model of a _____ carbon atom

3.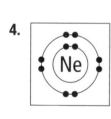

   (a) number of protons _____8_____

   (b) number of shells _____2_____

   (c) number of electrons _____8_____

   (d) number of valence electrons _____6_____

   (e) Bohr model of an _____ oxygen atom

4.

   (a) number of protons _____10_____

   (b) number of shells _____2_____

   (c) number of electrons _____10_____

   (d) number of valence electrons _____8_____

   (e) Bohr model of a _____ Neon atom

5. The four elements above are in the same period. What do you notice about the number of shells for elements belonging to the same period?

   _____ the all only have two shells and non blut _____

   _____ neon's shells are full. _____

Use with textbook pages 64–67.

The periodic table and atomic theory

Use the following Bohr model to answer questions 1 to 6.

Match the Term on the left with the corresponding Number on the right. Each Number may be used more than once. Refer to the diagram above.

Term	Number
1. __4__ number of shells	**A.** 0
2. __19__ number of protons	**B.** 1
3. __19__ total number of electrons	**C.** 2
4. __1__ number of valence electrons	**D.** 3
5. __1__ number of electron(s) it has to lose to become stable	**E.** 4
6. __3__ number of shells holding the maximum number of electrons	**F.** 19
	G. 20

Circle the letter of the best answer.

7. What is the maximum number of electrons that the first electron shell can hold?

   A. 1

   B. 2

   C. 4

   D. 8

Use the periodic table on page 202 to answer questions 8 to 12.

8. How many electrons are in the outermost shell of a sulphur (S) atom?

   A. 1

   B. 2

   C. 6

   D. 7

9. How many electrons are in the outermost shell of a fluorine (F) ion?

   A. 1

   B. 2

   C. 7

   D. 8

10. How many shells are there in the Bohr model of an aluminum (Al) atom?

   A. 1

   B. 2

   C. 3

   D. 4

11. Which of the following represents the Bohr model electron arrangement of a chlorine (Cl) atom?

   A. 2, 15

   B. 2, 2, 13

   C. 2, 8, 7

   D. 2, 8, 8

12. What do a beryllium (Be) ion and a neon (Ne) atom have in common?

   A. They have full outer shells.

   B. They have the same number of electrons.

   C. They have the same number of electron shells.

   D. None of the above

Compounds

Textbook pages 76–83

Before You Read

What do you know about ions? Write your ideas on the lines below.

_____

_____

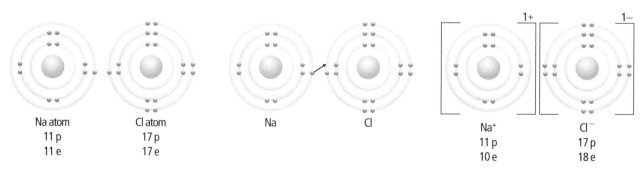

Na atom	Cl atom	Na	Cl	Na$^+$	Cl$^-$
11 p	17 p			11 p	17 p
11 e	17 e			10 e	18 e

Sodium (Na) loses an electron to chlorine (Cl) to form sodium chloride, an ionic compound. Sodium chloride is table salt.

Mark the Text

Identify Definitions

Highlight the definition of each word that appears in bold type.

✔ **Reading Check**

1. When is an ionic compound formed?

_____

_____

_____

_____

_____

How do compounds form?

Recall that an element is a pure substance that is made up of one type of atom. A **compound** is a pure substance that is made up of two or more types of atoms that are joined together due to a chemical change. Water, sugar, and table salt are three examples of compounds.

Atoms are held together in compounds by chemical bonds. These chemical bonds are created by attractive forces between atoms. Chemical bonds are formed when atoms gain or lose electrons, or when they share electrons. Recall that an atom is electrically neutral. When an atom loses electrons it becomes positively charged. When an atom gains electrons it becomes negatively charged.

What are ionic compounds?

If atoms gain electrons from other atoms or lose electrons to other atoms, they form **ionic compounds**. Ionic compounds usually form between metals and non-metals. Why? The atoms in metals tend to lose electrons. So metals have a positive charge when they form ions. The atoms in non-metals tend to gain electrons. So non-metals have a negative charge when they form ions. ✔

How do ionic compounds form?

When atoms of a metal come near atoms of a non-metal, they may join together to form an ionic compound. Electrons from the metal atoms are transferred to the non-metal atoms to create oppositely charged ions that attract each other. For instance, think about what happens when a sodium atom (metal) comes near a chlorine atom (non-metal). The sodium atom loses an electron to form a positive ion, and the chlorine atom gains an electron to form a negative ion. The two oppositely-charged ions are attracted to each other.

Ionic compounds are made up of charged particles (ions), but the positive charges and the negative charges balance, so ionic compounds are neutral.

A repeating pattern of positive and negative ions in a compound is called an **ionic lattice**.

How do covalent compounds form?

Sometimes atoms share electrons instead of losing and gaining them. If atoms share electrons, they form covalent compounds. **Covalent compounds** form when non-metal atoms bond together by sharing their electrons. Since the electrons are shared, the particles that make up covalent compounds are neutral. They do not have a charge. A neutral particle that is made up of atoms that are joined together by covalent bonds is called a **molecule**. A water molecule is a covalent compound. Its molecules are made of hydrogen and oxygen. Carbon dioxide gas is also a covalent compound. Its molecules are made of carbon and oxygen. ✔

✔ Reading Check

2. When is a covalent compound formed?

_____

_____

_____

_____

_____

What is a polyatomic ion?

Some ions contain more than one atom. For example, the nitrate ion (NO_3^-) contains nitrogen and oxygen. The carbonate ion (CO_3^{2-}) contains carbon and oxygen. In these many-atom ions, the atoms are held together with covalent bonds. But the many-atom unit has a charge, so it is considered an ion. An ion that is made up of two or more atoms that are held together with covalent bonds is called a **polyatomic ion**.

Use with textbook pages 76–80.

Words to know about compounds

Vocabulary	
atom	ionic lattice
chemical bonds	lose
~~compound~~	molecule
covalent compounds	negatively
electrons	neutrons
element	polyatomic ion
gain	positively
ion	protons
ionic compounds	

Use the terms in the vocabulary box to fill in the blanks. Each term may be used more than once. You will not need to use every term.

1. A pure substance that is made up of one type of atom is called a(n)

   _____.

2. A pure substance that is made up of two or more types of atoms that are joined together due to a chemical change is called a(n) _____.

3. Atoms in a molecule and ions in an ionic lattice are held together by

   _____.

4. Chemical bonds are formed when atoms gain or lose _____
   or when they share_____.

5. When an atom loses electrons it becomes _____ charged.
   When an atom gains electrons it becomes _____ charged.

6. Metals and non-metals may form _____.

7. The atoms in non-metals tend to _____ electrons.

8. A(n) _____ is a repeating pattern of
   positive and negative ions.

9. _____ form when non-metal atoms bond together
   by sharing their electrons.

10. A neutral particle that is made up of atoms that are joined together by covalent bonds
    is called a(n) _____.

11. A(n) _____ is an ion that is made up of
    two or more atoms that are held together with covalent bonds.

Name _____ Date _____

Comprehension

Section 3.1

Use with textbook pages 76–80.

True or false?

Read the statements given below. If the statement is true, write "T" on the line in front of the statement. If it is false, write "F" and rewrite the statement to make it true.

1. _____ An element is a pure substance made of more than one kind of compound.

   _____

2. _____ Compounds form through chemical bonds.

   _____

3. _____ In covalent compounds, atoms gain or lose electrons to form molecules.

   _____

4. _____ Water is a molecule formed by the sharing of electrons between the atoms of hydrogen and oxygen.

   _____

   _____

5. _____ Covalent compounds involve the sharing of electrons, while ionic compounds involve the transfer of electrons.

   _____

   _____

6. _____ Ions are formed when atoms lose or gain protons.

   _____

7. _____ An ionic lattice is a repeating pattern of positive and negative ions.

   _____

   _____

8. _____ A polyatomic ion is electrically neutral.

   _____

9. _____ Atoms are held together by covalent bonds in polyatomic ions.

   _____

   _____

© 2007 McGraw-Hill Ryerson Limited

Section 3.1   **Compounds • MHR**   **41**

Use with textbook pages 76–80.

Comparing ionic and covalent compounds

Use the chart to help you compare ionic compounds and covalent compounds. On the left side, place the letters of the statements that are only true of ionic compounds. On the right side, place the letters of the statements that are only true of covalent compounds. In the middle, place the letters of the statements that are true of both compounds.

A. atoms gain or lose electrons to form ions

B. pure substance made up of two or more kinds of elements

C. compound is made of a positive ion and a negative ion

D. atoms join by sharing electrons

E. atoms are joined to each other by chemical bonds

F. exist as a solid in the form of an ionic lattice

G. oppositely charged ions attract each other

H. molecule made of uncharged atoms

I. bond between atoms is due to electron transfer

J. compound is made of a non-metal and a non-metal

K. sodium chloride (NaCl) is an example

L. water (H_2O) is an example

Ionic compound	Both	Covalent compound

Use with textbook pages 76–80.

Compounds

Match each Term on the left with the best Descriptor on the right. Each Descriptor may be used only once.	
Term	**Descriptor**
1. _____ molecule	**A.** pure substance made of one type of atom
2. _____ ionic lattice	
3. _____ polyatomic ion	**B.** atoms combine by gaining or losing electrons
4. _____ ionic compound	
5. _____ covalent compound	**C.** repeating pattern of positive and negative ions
	D. atoms combine by sharing electrons to form molecules
	E. neutral particle that is made up of atoms that are joined together by covalent bonds
	F. ion made up of two or more atoms that are held together with covalent bonds

Circle the letter of the best answer.

6. Atoms in non-metals tend to gain

  A. molecules

  B. ions

  C. atoms

  D. electrons

7. Which of the following can be formed when there is electron transfer between metals and non-metals?

  A. molecule

  B. element

  C. ionic bond

  D. covalent bond

8. Which of the following is formed due to the sharing of electrons between two non-metals?

I.	a molecule
II.	a covalent bond
III.	a covalent compound

  A. I and II only

  B. I and III only

  C. II and III only

  D. I, II, and III

9. Water is a(n)

  A. element

  B. polyatomic ion

  C. ionic compound

  D. covalent compound

10. Sodium chloride is a(n)

  A. element

  B. polyatomic ion

  C. ionic compound

  D. covalent compound

11. Which of the following can be formed when a non-metal atom reacts with a non-metal atom?

  A. element

  B. polyatomic ion

  C. ionic compound

  D. covalent compound

Names and Formulas of Ionic Compounds

Textbook pages 84–95

Before You Read

How do ionic compounds form? Write your ideas on the lines below.

_____

_____

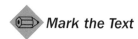

Mark the Text

Check for Understanding

As you read this section, be sure to reread any parts you do not understand. Highlight any sentences that help you develop your understanding.

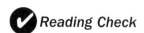

Reading Check

1. What does a chemical formula include?

_____

_____

Reading Check

2. What is a multivalent metal?

_____

_____

How are ionic compounds named and represented?

The **chemical formula** of an ionic compound includes symbols that identify each ion in the compound. The chemical formula also uses a subscript number to the right of an element symbol to show the relative numbers of ions in the compound. The **chemical names** of some ionic compounds include **Roman numerals**—for example, iron(III) sulphide. These ionic compounds include **multivalent metals**—metals that can form two or more different positive ions with different charges. ✔

Steps for naming ionic compounds with two elements

Steps	Example: CaF_2
1. Name the metal ion.	Ca is calcium.
2. Name the non-metal ion, but change the end of its name to "ide."	F is fluorine. Change it to fluoride.
3. Put the names together.	calcium fluoride

Steps for writing formulas of ionic compounds with two elements

Steps	Example: zinc nitride
1. Identify each ion and its charge.	zinc: Zn^{2+} nitride: N^{3-}
2. Determine the total charges needed to balance positive and negative ions.	Zn^{2+}: +2 +2 +2 = +6 N^{3-}: −3 −3 = −6
3. Note the ratio of positive to negative.	3 Zn^{2+} ions for every 2 N^{3-} ions.
4. Use subscripts to write the formula. A "1" is not shown in the subscript.	Zn_3N_2

Steps for writing formulas of compounds with a multivalent metal

Steps	Example: iron(III) sulphide
1. Identify each ion and its charge.	iron(III): Fe^{3+} sulphide: S^{2-}
2. Determine the total charges needed to balance positive and negative ions.	Fe^{3+}: $+3 +3 = +6$ S^{2-}: $-2 -2 -2 = -6$
3. Note the ratio of positive to negative.	2 Fe^{3+} ions for every 3 S^{2-} ions.
4. Use subscripts to write the formula.	Fe_2S_3

Steps for naming ionic compounds containing a multivalent metal

Steps	Examples	
	Cu_3P	**MnO_2**
1. Identify the metal.	copper (Cu)	manganese (Mn)
2. Verify that it can form more than one kind of ion by checking the periodic table.	Cu^{2+} and Cu^+	Mn^{2+}, Mn^{3+}, and Mn^{4+}
3. Determine the ratio of the ions in the formula.	Cu_3P means 3 copper ions for every 1 phosphide ion.	MnO_2 means 1 manganese ion for every 2 oxide ions.
4. Note the charge of the negative ion from the periodic table.	The charge on the phosphide P^{3-} is 3−.	The charge on the oxide O^{2-} is 2−.
5. The positive and negative charges must balance out. Determine what the charge needs to be on the metal ion to balance the negative ion.	Each of the 3 copper ions must have a charge of 1+ to balance the 1 phosphide ion with a charge of 3−. Therefore, the name of the copper ion is copper(I).	The 1 manganese ion must have a charge of 4+ to balance the 2 oxide ions that each have a charge of 2−. Therefore, the name of the manganese ion is manganese(IV).
6. Write the name of the compound.	copper(I) phosphide	manganese(IV) oxide

Steps for writing the formula of a compound with polyatomic ions

Steps	Examples	
	iron(III) hydroxide	**ammonium carbonate**
1. Identify each ion and its charge.	iron(III): Fe^{3+} hydroxide: OH^-	ammonium: NH_4^+ carbonate: CO_3^{2-}
2. Determine the total charges needed to balance positive with negative.	Fe^{3+}: $3+$ OH^-: $-1 -1 -1$	NH_4^+: $+1 +1$ CO_3^{2-}: $2-$
3. Note the ratio of positive ions to negative ions.	1 Fe^{3+} ion for every 3 OH^- ions	2 NH_4^+ ions for every 1 CO_3^{2-} ion
4. Use subscripts and brackets to write the formula. Omit brackets if only one ion is needed.	$Fe(OH)_3$	$(NH_4)_2CO_3$

Use with textbook pages 84–92.

Writing names and formulas of ionic compounds

You can use the periodic table on page 202 to help you answer these questions.

1. Complete the following table. First, identify each ion and its charge. Then, give the formula and name for each ionic compound formed. The table has been partially completed to help guide you.

	Chloride Cl-	Fluoride F-	Oxygen O^{-2}
sodium Na+	NaCl sodium chloride	Na F Sodium Fluoride	$Na_2 O_1$ sodium Oxygen
magnesium Mg^{+2}	Mg_1Cl_2 Magnesium chloride	$Mg_1 F_2$ magnesium fluoride	Mg O Magnesium oxygen
calcium Ca^{+2}	$Ca_1 Cl_2$ calcium chloride	$Ca_1 F_2$ Calcium Fluoride	Ca O calcium oxygen

2. Write the names of the following compounds.

(a) KCl _Potassium chloride_

(b) LiBr _Lithium Bromide_

(c) BaF$_2$ _Barium Floride$_2$_

(d) Ag$_3$P _Silver$_3$ Phosphorus_

(e) ZnS _Zinc Sulphide_

(f) SrO _strontiom Oxygen_

(g) AlCl$_3$ _Aluminum Chloride$_3$_

(h) Mg$_2$C _Magnesium$_2$ Carbon_

3. Write the chemical formulas for the following compounds.

(a) beryllium sulphide _Be S_

(b) silver oxide _Ag O_

(c) sodium bromide _N$_1$ Br_

(d) zinc chloride _Zn Cl_

(e) calcium sulphide _Ca S_

(f) lithium nitride _Li N_

(g) rubidium chloride _Rb Cl_

(h) germanium bromide _Ge Br_

Use with textbook pages 84–92.

Compounds with a multivalent metal

You can use the periodic table on page 202 to help you answer these questions.

1. Write the formulas for the compounds formed from the following ions. Then name the compounds.

	Ions	Formula	Compound name
(a)	Mn^{3+} O^{2-}	Mn_2O_3	Manganese Oxide
(b)	Pb^{3+} Br^-	Pb_1Br_3	lead bromide
(c)	Pt^{2+} Cl^-	Pt_1Cl_2	Platinum Cloride
(d)	Au^{3+} S^{2-}	Au_2S_3	Gold Sulphide
(e)	Pb^{4+} O^{2-}	Pb_2O_4	lead Oxide
(f)	Sb^{3+} S^{2-}	Sb_2S_3	Antimony sulphide
(g)	Fe^{2+} S^{2-}	FeS	iorn solphide
(h)	Co^{3+} O^{2-}	Co_2O_3	Cobalt oxide

2. Write the names of the following ionic compounds using Roman numerals.

(a) FeF_3 _____

(b) $CuCl_2$ _____

(c) SnO_2 _____

(d) PtS_2 _____

(e) $CoBr_2$ _____

(f) Au_2O _____

(g) CrP _____

(h) PbI_2 _____

3. Write the chemical formulas for the following compounds.

(a) iron(III) chloride _____

(b) copper(I) oxide _____

(c) tin(IV) sulphide _____

(d) bismuth(V) chloride _____

(e) gold(I) oxide _____

(f) chromium(II) fluoride _____

(g) manganese(II) iodide _____

(h) iron(III) selenide _____

Use with textbook pages 84–92.

Compounds with polyatomic ions

You can use the periodic table on page 202 to help you answer these questions.

1. Write the names of the following ionic compounds.

   (a) $AgNO_3$ _silver Nitrogen Oxide_   (e) $Ni(OH)_2$ _Nikel Hydroxide_

   (b) $BaSO_4$ _Barium Sulfate_   (f) $CuCO_3$ _Copper Carbonate_

   (c) NH_4Cl _Ammonium chloride_   (g) $Sr(NO_3)_2$ _Strontium Nitrogen Oxide_

   (d) $Ca_3(PO_4)_2$ _Calcium Phosphate_   (h) $Cr_2(SO_4)_3$ _Chromium sulfate_

2. Write the chemical formulas for the following compounds.

   (a) calcium hydroxide _$Ca_2 OH$_   (e) potassium dichromate _$K(Cr_2O_7)$_

   (b) ammonium chloride _$NH_4 Cl$_   (f) tin(II) hydroxide _____

   (c) sodium nitrite _$Na NO$_   (g) ammonium phosphate _$NH_4(PO_4)$_

   (d) lithium hydrogen carbonate _$Li(HCa)$_   (h) iron(III) nitrate _Fe_

3. Write the formulas and names of the compounds with the following combination of ions. The table has been partially completed to help guide you.

	Positive ion	Negative ion	Formula	Compound name
(a)	Ca^{2+}	CO_3^{2-}	$CaCO_3$	calcium carbonate
(b)	K^+	SO_3^{2-}	KSO_3	Potasium Sulphur Oxide
(c)	Na^+	ClO	$NaClO_3$	Sodium Chlorine Oxide
(d)	Mg^{2+}	ClO_4^{-1}	$MgClO_4$	magnesium perchlorate
(e)	Cs^+	OH^-	$CsOH$	hydroxide
(f)				ammonium phosphate
(g)			$Ca(CN)_2$	cyanide
(h)	Fe^{3+}	HSO_4^-		

Use with textbook pages 84–92.

Names and formulas of ionic compounds

Match each Compound Name on the left with the correct Chemical Formula on the right. Each Chemical Formula may be used only once.	
Compound Name	**Chemical Formula**
1. _____ aluminum sulphide	**A.** Al_2S_3
2. _____ aluminum sulphate	**B.** $AlSO_4$
3. _____ ammonium sulphite	**C.** $Al_2(SO_3)_3$
	D. $Al_2(SO_4)_3$
	E. NH_4SO_3
	F. NH_4SO_4
	G. $(NH_4)_2SO_3$
	H. $(NH_4)_2SO_4$

Circle the letter of the best answer.

4. How many chlorine atoms are in the compound calcium chlorate, $Ca(ClO_3)_2$?

   A. 1

   B. 2

   C. 3

   D. 6

5. What is the ending of an ionic compound consisting of two elements (a metal and a non-metal)?

   A. ate

   B. ide

   C. ine

   D. ite

6. In a chemical formula, what part shows the relative numbers of ions in the compound?

   A. the coefficient in front of the element symbol

   B. the subscript to the right of the element symbol

   C. the superscript to the right of the element symbol

   D. the positive or negative number to the right of the element symbol

Use the following diagrams to answer question 7.

26	3+
Fe	2+
Iron	
55.8	

25	2+
Mn	3+
Manganese	4+
54.9	

7. What do iron and manganese have in common?

I.	they are multivalent metals
II.	they have more than one ion charge
III.	their most common ion charge is 2+

   A. I and II only

   B. I and III only

   C. II and III only

   D. I, II, and III

8. In the name "cobalt(II) phosphate," what does the Roman numeral reveal about cobalt?

   A. it has gained two electrons

   B. it has an ion charge of 2–

   C. it has an ion charge of 2+

   D. it can form two positive ions

9. What is the name for the compound $CaCl_2$?

   A. calcium chlorate

   B. calcium chloride

   C. calcium chlorine

   D. calcium(II) chloride

Physical and Chemical Changes

Textbook pages 96–105

Before You Read

Cooking an egg is a chemical change. Boiling water is a physical change. What do you think is the difference between a chemical change and a physical change?

_____

_____

 Mark the Text

Reinforce Your Understanding

As you read this section, highlight the main point of each paragraph. Use a different colour to highlight an example that helps explain the main point, or write your own.

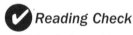 **Reading Check**

1. What is formed in a chemical change?

_____

_____

_____

What is a physical change?

During a **physical change**, a substance changes in form but not in its chemical composition. No new substances are formed. Ice melting is an example of a physical change. Some of the properties of liquid water are different from the properties of solid water. But the chemical composition of the water has not changed and no new substances have been produced.

All changes of state are physical changes. Other physical changes include cutting, grinding, and tearing substances. Dissolving salt in water is also a physical change. The individual salt ions and water molecules do not change when salt is dissolved in water.

What is a chemical change?

A **chemical change** causes one or more new substances to be formed.

Burning paper is an example of a chemical change. The smoke that escapes and the grey-black solid that is left behind (ash) are new substances. Each new substance has properties and chemical compositions that are different from the original paper.

In any chemical change, the starting substances that react are called reactants, and the substances that result are called products.

In a chemical change, new chemical bonds are formed while other chemical bonds are broken.✔

How can you tell if a change is chemical?

Some chemical changes are easy to observe. When fireworks explode, energy is released in the form of heat, light, and sound. Other chemical changes may be more difficult to observe.

If you can make two or more of the following observations, then a chemical change probably has taken place.

◆ Heat is produced or absorbed.

◆ One or both reactants are used up.

◆ There is a change in colour.

◆ Gas bubbles form in a liquid.

◆ A solid forms in a liquid.

How is energy involved with physical and chemical changes?

All changes in matter involve changes in energy. Energy is either released or absorbed. The energy is often in the form of heat, but it also may be in the form of sound or light.

If energy is released, the process is described as **exothermic**. Water freezing, iron rusting, and natural gas burning are examples of exothermic changes. If energy is absorbed, the process is described as **endothermic**. Cooking an egg, baking bread, and melting ice are examples of endothermic changes. ✔

 Reading Check

2. In what kind of process is energy absorbed?

_____

_____

Use with textbook pages 96–100.

Evidence of chemical change

Vocabulary	
changes of state	light
chemical	liquid
endothermic	physical
energy	product
exothermic	reactant
gas bubbles	solid
heat	sound

Use the terms in the vocabulary box to fill in the blanks. Each term may be used more than once. You will not need to use every term.

1. A(n) _chemical_ ✓ change produces new substances with new properties. An example of this would be rust forming on an iron nail.

2. In a(n) _physical_ ✓ change, the appearances of substances change, but no new substances are produced. An example of this would be the melting of a chocolate bar.

3. All _changes of state_ ✓ (for example, boiling, freezing, and melting) are physical changes because they do not produce new substances.

4. Dissolving salt in water is an example of a(n) _physical_ ✓ change. Burning paper is an example of a(n) _chemical_ ✓ change.

5. When baking soda is added to vinegar, a gas is formed. In this example, baking soda is a(n) _reactant_ ✓ and the gas formed is called the _product_ ✓.

6. In a chemical reaction, _solid_ ✓ or a(n) _gas bubbles_ ✓ might form in a liquid.

7. An explosion is an example of a(n) _exothermic_ ✓ process. The energy released in this type of reaction is usually in the form of _heat_ ✓, _light_ ✓, or _sound_ ✓.

8. In a(n) _endothermic_ ✓ process, energy is absorbed from the surrounding environment.

$\frac{13}{13}$

Use with textbook pages 96–100.

Chemical change and physical change

1. Define the following terms.

   (a) chemical change _creates new substance with new properties_

   (b) physical change _the substance only changes form no new substances are made_

2. Identify whether the example is a physical change or a chemical change.

   (a) ice cream melting _physical_

   (b) rust forming on a car _chemical_

   (c) a tire inflating with air _physical_

   (d) food digesting in the stomach _chemical_

   (e) cutting a piece of paper into two pieces _physical_

   (f) acid on limestone producing carbon dioxide gas _chemical_

3. For a slice of bread and a piece of wood, draw an example of each of the following changes.

   (a) A slice of bread—physical change

   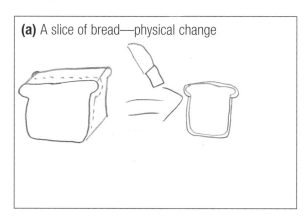

   (b) A slice of bread—chemical change

   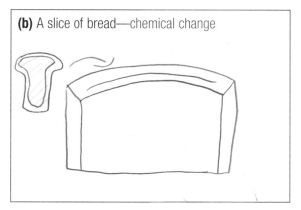

   (c) A piece of wood—physical change

   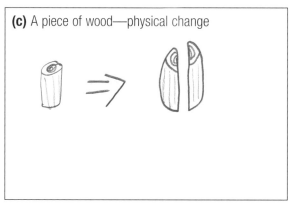

   (d) A piece of wood—chemical change

   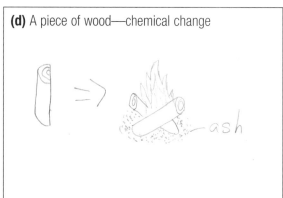

Name Cassie Berg   Date

Use with textbook pages 96–100.

enter   exit

Endothermic or exothermic?

1. Define the following terms.

    (a) exothermic ___when energy is released___

    _____

    (b) endothermic ___when energy is absorbed___

    _____

2. What type of process—exothermic or endothermic—is shown in each illustration?

(a) ___exothemic___   (b) ___endothermic___

3. Identify each of the following changes as exothermic or endothermic by placing a checkmark in the correct box.

	Description	Exothermic	Endothermic
(a)	ice melting		✓
(b)	water boiling		✓
(c)	water freezing	✓	
(d)	dynamite exploding	✓	
(e)	fireworks lighting up the sky	✓	
(f)	trees burning during a forest fire	✓	
(g)	cold pack used for an injury		✓
(h)	gasoline burning in an engine	✓	
(i)	match burning after it is rubbed on a rough surface	✓	

Use with textbook pages 96–100.

Physical and chemical changes

Match each Term on the left with the best Descriptor on the right. Each Descriptor may be used only once.	
Term	**Descriptor**
1. _E_ physical change	**A.** heat is given off
2. _D_ chemical change	**B.** heat is absorbed
3. _A_ exothermic	**C.** does not involve heat
4. _B_ endothermic	**D.** new products are formed
	E. appearance of substance changes

Circle the letter of the best answer.

5. Which of the following is an example of a physical change?

   A. a glacier melting

   B. a campfire burning

   C. an antacid tablet fizzing after it is placed in water

   D. carbon dioxide being produced in the engine of a running car

6. Which of the following is an example of a chemical change?

   A. a lake freezing over

   B. grinding rocks into gravel

   C. sugar dissolving in a cup of tea

   D. a candle burning

7. When an iron nail is left out in the rain, the iron combines with oxygen in the air to form iron (III) oxide, which is commonly known as rust. What do the iron and oxygen represent?

   A. the products

   B. the reactants

   C. the physical change

   D. the chemical change

8. A student adds a white powder to a clear liquid and the mixture begins to bubble. The student notices that the side of the container feels warm. What is this an example of?

I.	a physical change
II.	a chemical change
III.	an exothermic reaction
IV.	an endothermic reaction

   A. I and III only

   B. I and IV only

   C. II and III only

   D. II and IV only

9. Which of the following are evidence that a chemical change has occurred?

I.	a colour change
II.	a solid forms
III.	bubbles of gas form

   A. I and II only

   B. I and III only

   C. II and III only

   D. I, II, and III

The Function of the Nucleus within the Cell

Textbook pages 122–135

Before You Read

Which parts of the cell bring in food and get rid of waste? Which parts of a cell control its ability to grow, develop, and make new cells? Record your ideas on the lines below.

_____

_____

Create an Outline

Make an outline of the information in this section. Use the headings in the reading and the labels in the diagrams to help you. Include the boldface terms and any other terms that you think are important.

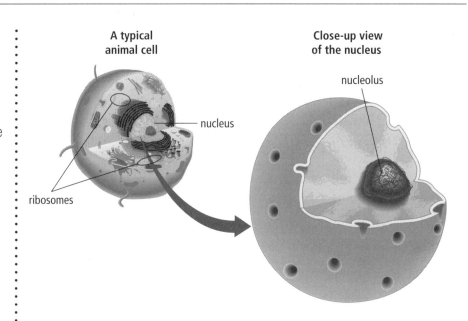

A typical animal cell — nucleus, ribosomes

Close-up view of the nucleus — nucleolus

What does the cell nucleus do?

The **nucleus** is the control centre of the cell. This means that the nucleus directs and controls all of the cell's activities. These activities include the ability of the cell to grow, develop, and replicate (make copies of itself).

How does the nucleus perform its job?

In the nucleus, the instructions for how to perform all cell activities are carried in molecules of **DNA**. DNA is a long, two-stranded molecule with a shape like a ladder that has been twisted into a spiral. DNA stores instructions for how to form cells, for the chemicals and structures that cells must make, and for everything that the cell does. DNA also stores genetic material—information that is passed on from one generation to another when organisms reproduce. ✔

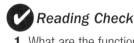 Reading Check

1. What are the functions of DNA?

_____

_____

_____

_____

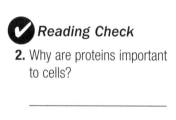

How is DNA related to chromosomes and genes?

Strands of DNA are packaged tightly into structures called **chromosomes**. Each type of organism has a specific number of chromosomes. For example, humans have 46 chromosomes that are arranged in 23 pairs. One of these pairs helps determine if a person will be born as a male or a female.

   Genes are found at specific places on a chromosome. **Genes** are small segments of DNA that carry instructions for making proteins. **Proteins** are molecules that all the cells of the body need in order to work properly. Some proteins carry out cell functions. Other proteins are parts of cell structures. There are as many as 100 000 proteins in the human body. ✔

Where are proteins made?

Proteins are made in the cell by **ribosomes**. Ribosomes are made by a large structure in the nucleus called the **nucleolus**.

✔ *Reading Check*

2. Why are proteins important to cells?

_____

_____

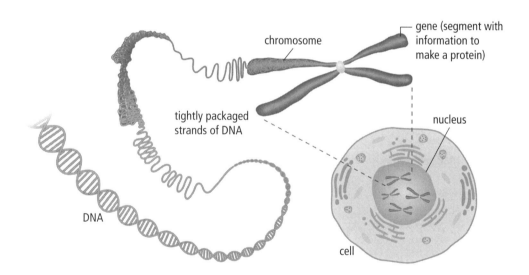

This illustration shows DNA packaged in a chromosome, and the chromosome in the nucleus.

Use with textbook pages 123–129.

Inside the nucleus

Vocabulary	
~~23~~	~~nucleolus~~
~~46~~	~~nucleus~~
~~chromosomes~~	~~number~~
~~DNA~~	proteins
genes	~~ribosomes~~
~~genetic~~	type
~~molecule~~	

Use the terms in the vocabulary box to fill in the blanks. Each term may be used more than once. You will not need to use every term.

1. The _nucleus_ directs and controls the ability of the cell to grow, develop, and replicate (make copies of itself).

2. The instructions for how to carry out all cell activities are carried in _DNA_, which is a long, two-stranded _molecule_ with a shape like a ladder that has been twisted into a spiral shape.

3. _DNA_ stores instructions for everything that the cell does. It also stores _genetic_ material—information that is passed on from one generation to another when organisms reproduce.

4. Strands of DNA are packaged tightly into structures called _chromosomes_.

5. Each type of organism has a specific _number_ of chromosomes.

6. Humans have _46_ chromosomes that are arranged in _23_ pairs. One of these pairs helps determine if a person will be born as a male or a female.

7. _Genes_ are small segments of DNA that carry instructions for making proteins. They are found at specific places on _chromosomes_.

8. Proteins are a type of _molecule_ that all the cells of the body need in order to work properly.

9. Proteins are made in the cell by _ribosomes_, which are made by a large structure in the nucleus called the _nucleolus_.

Name _____ Date _____

Use with textbook pages 125–130.

The control centre of the cell

Use the diagram to help you answer question 1.

1. Describe the structure of DNA.

long two strandes with a ladder shape that has
been twisted into a spiral

_____

Fill in the blanks with the correct terms. Then use your answers to questions 2–5 to label the diagram below.

2. The control centre of the cell _is the nucleus_

3. Molecule containing instructions for everything the cell does _DNA_

4. Tightly packaged structures of DNA _chromosomes_

5. Segment with information to make a protein _Genes_

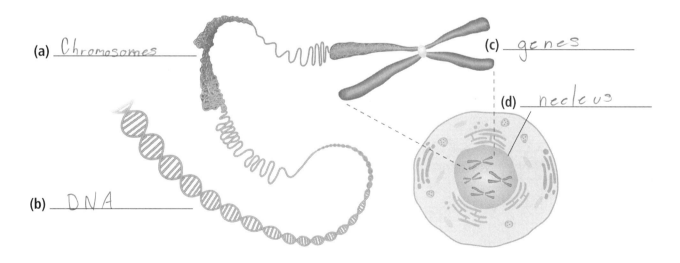

(a) _Chromosomes_

(b) _DNA_

(c) _genes_

(d) _necleus_

Use with textbook pages 131–132.

True or false?

Read the statements given below. If the statement is true, write "T" on the line in front of the statement. If it is false, write "F" and rewrite the statement to make it true.

1. ___F___ The nucleolus directs and controls all of the cell's activities.

   The nucleous directs and controles...

2. ___T___ Instructions for how to carry out all cell activities are carried in molecules of DNA.

   _____

   _____

3. ___T___ DNA stores information that is passed on from one generation to another when organisms reproduce.

   _____

   _____

4. ___F___ Humans have 46 pairs of chromosomes.

   Humans have 2 3 pairs of chromosomes

5. ___T___ One pair of ribosomes helps determine if a person will be born as a male or female.

   _____

   _____

6. ___T___ The nucleolus makes ribosomes.

   _____

7. ___T___ Ribosomes make proteins.

   _____

8. ___F___ Genes make chromosomes.

   Genes make protins

Use with textbook pages 121–132.

The function of the nucleus within the cell

Match each Term on the left with the best Descriptor on the right. Each Descriptor may be used only once.	
Term	**Descriptor**
1. _G_ chromosome	**A.** segment of DNA located at a specific place on a chromosome
2. _C_ DNA	
3. _A_ gene	
4. _F_ nucleolus	**B.** controls all the activities within a cell
5. _B_ nucleus	**C.** a molecule found in the cell nucleus that carries genetic information
6. _D_ proteins	**D.** essential materials needed to carry out cell activities
	E. makes proteins
	F. makes ribosomes
	G. tightly packed structure of DNA

Circle the letter of the best answer.

7. Proteins are made by

   A. the ribosomes

   B. the chromosomes

   C. the DNA

   D. the nucleolus

8. Approximately how many proteins are in the human body?

   A. 100

   B. 1000

   C. 10 000

   D. 100 000

9. Which of the following are functions of proteins?

I.	carry out cell functions
II.	form parts of cell structures
III.	control all of the cells functions

   A. I and II only

   B. I and III only

   C. II and III only

   D. I, II, and III

10. What instructions do genes carry?

   A. to make proteins

   B. to determine whether a person will be born male or female

   C. to pass information from one generation to the next

   D. to store genetic material

11. How many chromosomes do humans have?

   A. chromosomes are too small to be counted

   B. between 90 000 and 100 000

   C. 92 arranged in 46 pairs

   D. 46 arranged in 23 pairs

12. Which of the following best describes DNA?

I.	twisted in a spiral shape
II.	shaped like a ladder
III.	long, two-stranded molecule

   A. I and II only

   B. I and III only

   C. II and III only

   D. I, II, and III

Mutations

Textbook pages 136–145

Before You Read

What do you think of when you read or hear the word "mutation?" Is mutation always harmful? Is mutation always helpful? Record your thoughts on the lines below.

_____

_____

Mark the Text

In Your Own Words

Highlight the main idea in each paragraph. Stop after each paragraph and put what you just read into your own words.

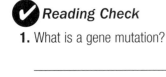
Reading Check

1. What is a gene mutation?

_____

_____

_____

What is a gene mutation?

A **gene mutation**, or mutation for short, is a change in the genetic material (DNA) of a gene. Changes to DNA may cause proteins to be made incorrectly or with an incorrect shape. Factors in the environment, called **mutagens**, can cause mutations. Radiation, such as X rays and UV rays, is an example of a mutagen. Cigarette smoke and other poisonous chemicals such as pesticides are also mutagens. ✔

Are mutations harmful?

Some mutations can be harmful to an organism. Harmful mutations are called **negative mutations**. For example, some people are born with a mutated gene that makes their red blood cells have a curved shape instead of the normal disc shape. The curved shape prevents the cells from carrying oxygen well and blocks blood flow in blood vessels.

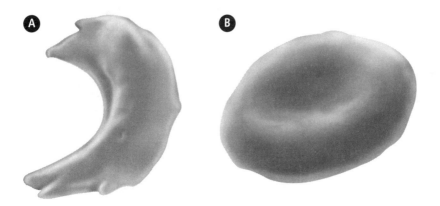

A mutated gene is responsible for red blood cells being curved (A) instead of disc shaped (B).

Some mutations can be helpful to an organism. Helpful mutations are called **positive mutations**. For example, some plants carry a mutated gene that protects them from certain diseases. Some people have a mutated gene that produces a special kind of protein. This protein prevents the virus called HIV from infecting the person. This type of mutation benefits an individual.

Most mutations have no effect on an organism. These mutations are called **neutral mutations**. For example, the Spirit Bears of coastal British Columbia have a mutated gene that makes their fur white instead of black. This mutation does not affect their lives in any important way. ✔

Can mutations be fixed?

Some mutations can be treated with drugs or surgery. New techniques for treating gene mutations are called **gene therapy.** In one form of gene therapy, researchers replace a mutated gene with a healthy copy of the gene. The healthy gene must first attach to a chromosome within a patient's cells. Then the gene needs to make the correct type and amount of protein. These techniques are still experimental at this time.

✔ *Reading Check*

2. List three types of gene mutations.

_____

_____

_____

Name _____ Date _____

Use with textbook pages 136–141.

Mutations concept map

Complete the following concept map about genetic mutations.

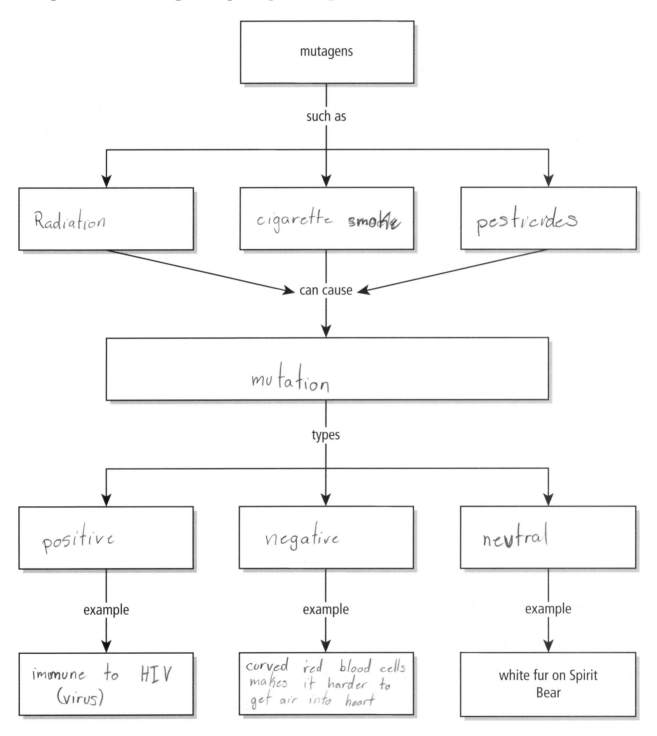

Use with textbook pages 136–143.

Gene mutation

Answer the questions below.

1. What is a gene mutation?

a change in the genetic material of a ~~gene~~ gene

2. Give the three types of gene mutations.

positive   neutral   negative

3. What type of mutation is beneficial to an organism?

positive

4. Give one example of a negative mutation.

sickle cell (anemia)

5. What type of mutation appears to have no effect on an organism?

neutral

6. What are mutagens?

something that causes a mutation

7. Give four examples of environmental mutagens.

~~radiation~~ Xray, UV ray, Cigarette smoke and
pesticides, pollutants, house hold cleaners

8. What are researchers doing to the mutated gene when they use gene therapy?

treating it with dugs or surgery (health gene)

Use with textbook pages 138–143.

The effects of mutations

Vocabulary	
DNA	~~negative mutations~~
~~gene mutation~~	~~neutral mutations~~
~~gene therapy~~	organism
~~healthy gene~~	~~positive mutations~~
~~mutagens~~	→~~proteins~~
~~mutated gene~~	

Use the terms in the vocabulary box to fill in the blanks. You will not need to use every term. You may use terms more than once.

1. A _____ *gean mutation* _____ is a change in the genetic material of a gene.

2. Changes to DNA may cause _____ *proteins* _____ to be made incorrectly or with an incorrect shape.

3. Factors in the environment, called _____ *mutagens* _____ can cause mutations.

4. Radiation, cigarette smoke, and pesticides are examples of _____ *mutagens* _____ .

5. Mutations that are harmful to an organism are called _____ *negative mutations* .

6. Mutations that are helpful to an organism are called _____ *positive mutations* _____ .
   For instance, some plants carry a mutated gene that protects them from disease.

7. Mutations that have no effect on an organism are called _____ *neutral mutation* .

8. New techniques for treating gene mutations are called _____ *gene therapy* _____
   and may involve replacing a _____ *mutated gene* _____
   with a _____ *healthy gene* _____ .

Use with textbook pages 136–143.

Mutation

Match each Term on the left with the best Descriptor on the right. Each Descriptor may be used only once.	
Term	**Descriptor**
1. _D_ gene mutation	**A.** techniques developed to replace mutated genes
2. _A_ gene therapy	**B.** a mutation that does not affect the organism
3. _G_ mutagens	**C.** a mutation that harms an organism
4. _C_ negative mutation	**D.** a change in the genetic material
5. _B_ neutral mutation	**E.** a mutation that benefits an organism
6. _E_ positive mutation	**F.** a healthy gene
	G. substance or factor that can cause mutations in DNA

Circle the letter of the best answer.

7. The coat colour of the Spirit Bear is due to

   A. change of the seasons

   B. global warming

   C. a mutated gene

   D. environmental stresses

8. Most mutations

   A. are helpful to the organism

   B. are harmful to the organism

   C. have no effect on the organism

   D. can be treated in an organism

9. Which of the following is an example of a neutral mutation?

I.	white fur instead of black fur
II.	a mutated gene protects a plant from a disease
III.	curved red blood cells instead of disc-shaped cells

   A. I

   B. II

   C. III

   D. none of the above

10. Which type of mutation is beneficial to an organism and, therefore, aids in the organism's ability to survive?

   A. neutral

   B. positive

   C. negative

   D. deletion

11. Errors in the DNA that appear to neither harm nor help an organism are called

   A. neutral

   B. positive

   C. negative

   D. substitutions

12. Which of the following can cause mutated genes?

I.	cigarette smoke
II.	radiation
III.	pesticides

   A. I and II only

   B. I and III only

   C. II and III only

   D. I, II, and III

The Cell Cycle and Mitosis

Textbook pages 150–165.

Before You Read

How do cells replace themselves? Record your ideas on the lines below.

_____

_____

 Mark the Text

Create a Chart

Highlight the text that describes the three stages of the cell cycle. In a different colour, highlight text that describes how cells divide. Use the highlighted text to create a chart about the life of a cell.

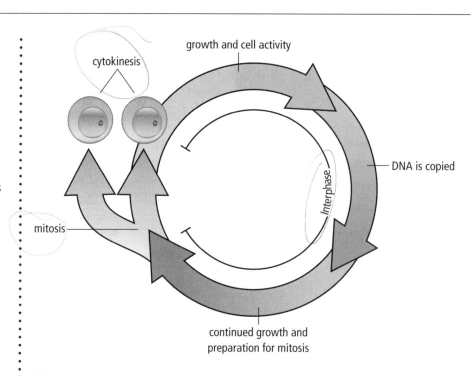

growth and cell activity

cytokinesis

DNA is copied

Interphase

mitosis

continued growth and preparation for mitosis

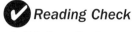 **Reading Check**

1. What are the three stages in the life of a cell?

_____

_____

_____

What is the cell cycle?

The three stages of the life of a cell together are called the **cell cycle**. These three stages are:

♦ **interphase**: This stage makes up most of the life of the cell. During interphase, cells grow and carry out their life functions. In cells that will divide, the nucleus makes a copy of its DNA in a process called **replication**.

♦ **mitosis**: During this stage, the nucleus of the cell divides into two equal and identical parts. Each part has a copy of the DNA.

♦ **cytokinesis**: During this stage, the two equal, identical parts of the cell separate. The result of this stage is two identical cells, each with a nucleus and DNA. ✔

What are the phases of mitosis?

There are four phases of mitosis. These phases are prophase, metaphase, anaphase, and telophase.

Phases of mitosis	What happens
prophase	• the duplicated chromosomes form into an X shape and the nucleolus disappears. • **spindle fibres**, which are tiny tube-like structures made of protein, begin to form in plant and animal cells
metaphase	• the duplicated chromosomes line up across the middle of the cell
anaphase	• the duplicated chromosomes move apart to opposite ends of the cell
telophase	• a nucleolus forms around the chromosomes at the opposite ends of the dividing cell

How can mutagens affect the cell cycle?

Mutagens can cause changes in the cell cycle so that cells keep dividing continuously. The cells pile up on top of one another, forming a lump called a tumour. The uncontrolled cell division sometimes results in diseases called **cancers**. Cancerous cells may grow in one place in the body, or they may spread to other parts of the body where they will continue to divide. ✔

Reading Check

2. What is cancer the result of?

_____

_____

_____

Use with textbook pages 153–158.

Getting to know the cell cycle

Vocabulary	
anaphase	~~mitosis~~
cell cycle	~~nucleolus~~
~~cytokinesis~~	nucleus
~~DNA~~	prophase
~~duplicated chromosomes~~	~~telophase~~
~~four~~	~~three~~
~~interphase~~	~~two~~
~~metaphase~~	

Use the terms in the vocabulary box to fill in the blanks. You can use each term more than once. You will not need to use every term.

1. There are _____three_____ stages in the life of a cell.

2. The stage that makes up most of the cell's life is ___inter phase___. During this stage, cells grow and carry out their life functions. In cells that will divide, the nucleus makes a copy of its ___DNA___.

3. During ___mitosis___, the nucleus of the cell divides into two equal and identical parts. Each part has a copy of the DNA.

4. During ___cytokinesis___, the two equal, identical parts of the cell separate. This stage forms ___two___ identical cells with a nucleus and DNA.

5. There are ___four___ phases of mitosis.

6. In ___metaphase___, the duplicated chromosomes contract into an X shape and the ___nucleolus___ disappears.

7. In ___metaphase___, the ___duplicated chromosomes___ line up across the middle of the cell.

8. In ___anaphase___, the ___duplicated chromosomes___ move apart to opposite ends of the cell.

9. In ___telophase___, a ___nucleolus___ forms around the chromosomes at the opposite ends of the dividing cell.

Name _____ Date _____

Use with textbook pages 150–165.

Identifying stages of the cell cycle

Vocabulary	
continued growth and preparation	growth and preparation
cytokinesis	interphase
replication	mitosis

Use the vocabulary words in the box above to label the stages of the cell cycle in the following diagram.

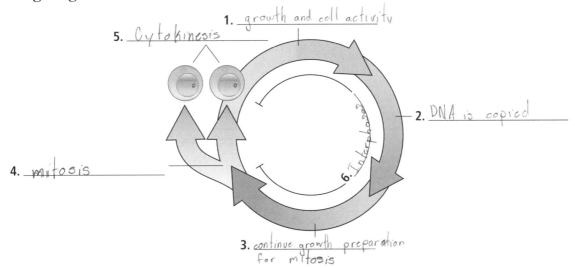

1. *growth and cell activity*
5. *Cytokinesis*
2. *DNA is copied*
4. *mitosis*
6. *Interphase*
3. *continue growth preparation for mitosis*

Briefly describe what is occurring in each stage of the cell cycle.

1. _____

_____

2. _____

_____

3. _____

_____

4. _____

_____

5. _____

_____

6. _____

_____

Use with textbook pages 156–157.

Mitosis

Summarize what is happening in the cell for each phase of mitosis. Then draw a labelled diagram of each phase.

Phase	What is happening in the cell?	Labelled diagram
prophase		
metaphase		
anaphase		
telophase		

Use with textbook pages 150–161.

The cell cycle and mitosis

Match each Term on the left with the best Descriptor on the right. Each Descriptor may be used only once.

Term	Descriptor
1. ___E___ cell cycle	A. first and longest stage of the cell cycle
2. ___F___ cytokinesis	B. process during which the cell copies DNA information in the nucleus
3. ___A___ interphase	C. result of uncontrolled cell division
4. ___D___ mitosis	D. process in which the duplicated contents of the cell's nucleus divide into two equal parts
5. ___B___ replication	E. three stages of the life of a cell
	F. final stage of the cell cycle, which separates the two nuclei and the cell contents into two identical cells

Circle the letter of the best answer.

6. Tiny tube-like structures made of protein are called
   A. spindle fibres
   B. chromosomes
   C. nucleolus
   D. DNA replication

7. Which stage is the longest in the cell cycle?
   A. interphase
   B. mitosis
   C. cytokinesis
   D. DNA replication

8. The phase of mitosis where the chromosomes line up across the middle of the cell is
   A. anaphase
   B. metaphase
   C. prophase
   D. telophase

9. The phase of mitosis in which the duplicated chromosomes form into an X shape is
   A. anaphase
   B. metaphase
   C. prophase
   D. telophase

10. The phase of mitosis in which duplicated chromosomes move apart to opposite ends of the cell is
    A. anaphase
    B. metaphase
    C. prophase
    D. telophase

11. The phase of mitosis in which a nucleolus forms around the chromosomes is
    A. anaphase
    B. metaphase
    C. prophase
    D. telophase

Asexual Reproduction

Textbook pages 166–183

Before You Read

What kinds of organisms reproduce by making exact copies of the parent organism? Give three or four examples on the lines below.

_____

_____

Create a Quiz

After you have read this section, create a five-question quiz based on what you have learned. After you have written the questions, be sure to answer them. Then share them with your classmates.

What is asexual reproduction?

Asexual reproduction is the formation of a new individual that has the same genetic information as its parent. The individual is a clone, or an exact copy, of its parent. Asexual reproduction occurs in one-celled organisms such as bacteria and in multicellular organisms such as plants.

What types of asexual reproduction are there?

There are several types of asexual reproduction, as shown in the table below.

Type of asexual reproduction	Definition	Examples of organisms that use this form of reproduction
binary fission	the splitting of a single parent cell into two equal parts that have the same copies of genetic material	• some kinds of bacteria • amoeba
budding	a group of rapidly dividing cells develops on an organism and breaks away to become a new organism	• some simple multicellular organisms such as hydras and sponges • one-celled yeasts
fragmentation	a small piece of an organism breaks away from it and develops into a new individual	• some plants, such as mosses and liverworts • some animals, such as some sea stars and corals
spore formation	parent organism produces spores: single cells that can develop into new individuals by repeated mitosis	• common in fungi • some plants and algae
vegetative reproduction	special cells, usually in the stems and roots of plants, divide repeatedly to form structures that develop into a plant that is identical to the parent	• very common in most kinds of plants

What are the advantages and disadvantages of asexual reproduction?

Advantages of asexual reproduction include:

◆ large colonies can out-compete other organisms for nutrients and water

◆ large numbers of offspring reproduce very quickly

◆ species can survive if the number of predators increases

Disadvantages of asexual reproduction include:

◆ offspring compete for food and space

◆ extreme temperatures can wipe out entire colonies

◆ negative mutations can destroy many offspring ✓

What technologies make use of asexual reproduction?

Humans can help other organisms reproduce asexually. This may be done to preserve the DNA of an organism. It may also be done to make large numbers of a particular type of organism that has a useful trait.

Growing new plants from the cut ends of plant stems and roots is one way that humans make clones of plants. Making clones of animals involves taking the nucleus from one type of cell and putting it into an egg cell that has had its nucleus removed. As the egg cell divides, its new cells have the DNA from the first type of cell.

Researchers are now using stem cells in cloning research. **Stem cells** are cells that can divide to form one of many different types of cells. Stem cells that come from human embryos can become any of the 200 types of cells in the human body. Stem cells that come from specific body tissues can become only a few types of body cells. Doctors are working to use stem cells to treat certain disorders such as diabetes and cancer. ✓

✓ Reading Check

1. What is one advantage of asexual reproduction?

_____

_____

_____

✓ Reading Check

2. What are stem cells?

_____

_____

_____

_____

Cloze
Activity

Section 5.2

Use with textbook pages 166–178.

Types of asexual reproduction

Vocabulary	
asexual reproduction	fragmentation
binary fission	grafts
budding	spore formation
clone	stem cells
cuttings	vegetative reproduction
DNA	

Use the terms in the vocabulary box to fill in the blanks. You can use each term more than once. You will not need to use every term.

1. A _____ is an identical genetic copy of its parent.

2. In _____, only one parent is required to produce offspring.

3. _____ is a method of reproduction for some types of bacteria.

4. Some simple organisms, such as hydras and sponges, are able to reproduce asexually by _____.

5. Certain species of sea stars, corals, and mosses can reproduce asexually by _____.

6. _____ occurs when special cells in the stems and roots divide repeatedly to form structures that eventually develop into a plant identical to the parent.

7. Some bacteria can reproduce asexually when their single cells split in two, forming new individuals in a process called _____.

8. Human-assisted cloning can be used to save the _____ of an organism or mass produce an organism with a desired trait.

9. _____ are cells that have the potential to become many different types of cells.

Use with textbook pages 168–175.

What are the five different types of asexual reproduction?

List the five types of asexual reproduction in the blanks below. Make a drawing to illustrate each type of asexual reproduction.

1. _____

2. _____

3. _____

4. _____

5. _____

Use with textbook pages 177–178.

True or false?

Read the statements given below. If the statement is true, write "T" on the line in front of the statement. If it is false, write "F" and then rewrite the statement to make it true.

1. _____ Asexual reproduction is the formation of a new individual that has different genetic information from its parent.

_____

_____

2. _____ Asexual reproduction occurs in multicellular organisms such as bacteria and in one-celled organisms such as plants.

_____

_____

3. _____ Sometimes humans help other organisms reproduce asexually in order to preserve the DNA of an organism.

_____

_____

4. _____ Sometimes humans help other organisms reproduce asexually to make large numbers of a particular type of organism that has a useful trait.

_____

_____

5. _____ Growing new plants from the cut ends of flowers is one way that humans make clones of plants.

_____

_____

6. _____ Making clones of animals involves taking the nucleus from one type of cell and putting it in the nucleus of another type of cell.

_____

_____

Use with textbook pages 166–178.

Asexual reproduction

Term	Descriptor
Match each Term on the left with the best Descriptor on the right. Each Descriptor may be used only once.	
1. _____ asexual reproduction	**A.** reproductive cells that develop into new individuals by repeated mitosis
2. _____ binary fission	**B.** a group of rapidly dividing cells develops on an organism and breaks away to become a new organism
3. _____ budding	
4. _____ clone	
5. _____ fragmentation	**C.** a form of asexual reproduction in which each fragment of an organism develops into a clone of its parent
6. _____ spores	
7. _____ vegetative reproduction	
	D. single parent cell splits into two equal parts that have the same copies of genetic material
	E. an identical genetic copy of an organism's parent
	F. only found in human embryos
	G. reproduction that requires only one parent
	H. root cells divide repeatedly to form structures that develop into a plant that is identical to the parent

Circle the letter of the best answer.

8. Asexual reproduction requires

 A. only one parent to produce offspring

 B. two parents to produce offspring

 C. a combination of parents to produce offspring

 D. two clones to produce offspring

9. Bacteria reproduce asexually by

 A. budding

 B. fragmentation

 C. binary fission

 D. cloning

10. Stem cells have the potential to

 A. divide rapidly

 B. increase the amount of DNA

 C. become many different types of cells

 D. invade other types of cells

11. During the process of cloning, scientists

 A. add more DNA to the parent cell

 B. remove the nucleus from an egg cell

 C. remove cytoplasm from an egg cell

 D. allow the egg cells to bud

12. One of the key advantages of asexual reproduction is

 A. offspring compete for food and space

 B. large numbers of offspring reproduce quickly

 C. extreme temperatures can wipe out entire colonies

 D. offspring are genetic clones

13. One of the disadvantages of asexual reproduction is

 A. species cannot survive when predators increase

 B. large colonies can out-compete other organisms for nutrients and water

 C. large numbers of offspring reproduce very slowly

 D. extreme temperatures can wipe out entire colonies

Meiosis

Textbook pages 188–203

Before You Read

Remind yourself: what happens during mitosis? Write your thoughts on the lines below.

_____

_____

State the Main Ideas

As you read this section, stop after each paragraph and put what you have just read into your own words.

✓ Reading Check

1. How many chromosomes are there in a human body cell?

_____

What is sexual reproduction?

In **sexual reproduction**, genetic information from two parent cells are passed on to an offspring. Female organisms and male organisms make specialized cells called **gametes**. Gametes from female parents are called eggs. Gametes from male parents are called sperm. In sexual reproduction, the gametes from the two parents combine during a process called **fertilization** to form a new cell. The new cell is called a **zygote**. The zygote is the first body cell of a new organism. As the zygote undergoes repeated mitosis and cell division, it matures into an **embryo**.

How do gametes differ from body cells?

All human body cells have 46 chromosomes. These chromosomes are arranged into 23 pairs. You receive one member of each pair of chromosomes from your mother. You receive the other member of each pair from your father.

When a cell has pairs of chromosomes, it is said to be *diploid*. Di- means two or double, referring to the two sets—the pairs—of chromosomes. Human body cells are diploid. Gamete cells, on the other hand, have only one set of chromosomes, for a total of 23 chromosomes. Gametes are said to be *haploid*. ✓

How do gametes become haploid?

In order for human body cells to remain diploid, gametes must have one half the number of chromosomes—that is, 23. Only haploid gametes with 23 chromosomes can combine during fertilization to form a diploid zygote with 46 chromosomes. **Meiosis** is the process that ensures that each gamete is haploid. In other words, meiosis produces gametes with one half the number of chromosomes as body cells.

The process of randomly dividing 23 pairs of chromosomes in half creates millions of possible combinations of chromosomes. Any of these combinations may be combined with chromosomes from the other parent in any gamete during fertilization. In this way, sexual reproduction and meiosis increase genetic diversity (variety) in a species.

What happens during meiosis?

Examine the diagram below. During meiosis, each chromosome in a cell is duplicated once and then the cell divides twice. The first division of the cell is called meiosis I. Meiosis I is similar to mitosis, but each pair of chromosomes includes one chromosome from each parent. These matching chromosomes are called **homologous chromosomes**. Meiosis I starts with a diploid cell and finishes with two haploid cells.

Each of the two haploid cells undergoes a second division called meiosis II. Meiosis II starts with two haploid cells and ends with four haploid cells. So the overall process of meiosis starts with one diploid cell and ends with four haploid cells.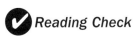

✔ **Reading Check**

2. In meiosis, how many haploid gamete cells result from one diploid parent cell?

_____

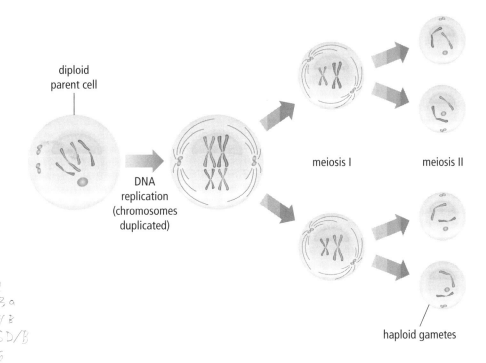

diploid parent cell

DNA replication (chromosomes duplicated)

meiosis I

meiosis II

haploid gametes

Use with textbook pages 188–190.

The role of gametes

1. Complete the table to show the number of chromosomes for different organisms. The table has been partially completed to help you.

Organism	Diploid number (2n)	Haploid number (n)
human		
fruit fly	8	
black bear		38
peanut	20	
chimpanzee		48

2. Use the terms in the box below to fill in the blanks in the meiosis flow chart. You can use each term more than once. You will not need to use every term.

Choices for chromosome number	Choices for other blanks
diploid	egg cell
haploid	female parent
	fertilization
	male parent
	sperm cell

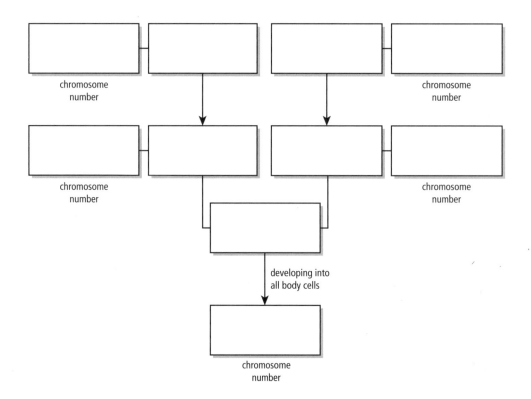

chromosome number

chromosome number

chromosome number

chromosome number

chromosome number

chromosome number

developing into all body cells

chromosome number

Use with textbook pages 191–193.

What happens in meiosis?

Vocabulary	
2	~~fertilization~~
3	~~gametes~~
~~4~~	~~haploid~~
~~23~~	meiosis
~~46~~	~~meiosis I~~
body cell	~~meiosis II~~
chromosome	~~mitosis~~
~~diploid~~	~~zygote~~
~~embryo~~	

Use the terms in the vocabulary box to fill in the blanks. You can use each term more than once. You will not need to use every term.

1. Female and male organisms produce specialized cells called __gametes__ that are necessary for reproduction. Eggs are the __gametes__ from female parents. Sperm are the __gametes__ from male parents.

2. During sexual reproduction, the gametes from the two parents combine during a process called __fertilization__ to form a new cell called a __zygote__.

3. As the zygote undergoes repeated __mitosis__ and cell division, it matures into a(n) __embryo__.

4. A human diploid body cell has __23__ pairs of chromosomes.

5. Human gamete cells have a total of __46__ chromosomes. Gametes are said to be __Haploid__.

6. During meiosis, each __Chromosome__ in a cell is duplicated once and then the cell divides twice.

7. The first division of the cell is called __meiosis I__, which starts with a diploid cell and finishes with two haploid cells.

8. Each of the two haploid cells undergoes a second division called __meiosis II__, which starts with two haploid cells and ends with four haploid cells.

9. Meiosis starts with one __diploid__ cell and ends with __4__ haploid cells.

Use with textbook page 194.

Comparing meiosis and mitosis

Examine the following diagrams showing mitosis and meiosis. Notice what happens to the chromosomes in each illustration. Then answer the questions that follow.

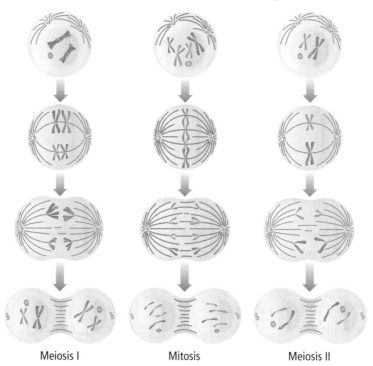

Meiosis I   Mitosis   Meiosis II

1. How is meiosis I similar to mitosis?

_____

_____

2. How is meiosis I different from mitosis?

_____

_____

3. How is meiosis II similar to mitosis?

_____

_____

4. How is meiosis II different from mitosis?

_____

_____

Use with textbook pages 188–202.

Meiosis

Match each Term on the left with the best Descriptor on the right. Each Descriptor may only be used once.	
Term	**Descriptor**
1. _____ diploid number 2. _____ embryo 3. _____ fertilization 4. _____ gametes 5. _____ genetic diversity 6. _____ haploid number 7. _____ homologous chromosomes 8. _____ sexual reproduction 9. _____ zygote	**A.** matching chromosomes **B.** process in which gametes from two parents combine **C.** two sets of chromosomes **D.** produces offspring that are genetically different from each other **E.** develops from a zygote **F.** new diploid cell formed by the process of fertilization **G.** the process of mitosis **H.** variety in a species **I.** one set of chromosomes **J.** specialized cells; sperm from males and eggs from females

Circle the letter of the best answer.

10. Human body cells have

   A. 17 chromosomes

   B. 23 chromosomes

   C. 46 chromosomes

   D. 92 chromosomes

11. The process of meiosis produces gametes with _____ as body cells.

   A. the same number of chromosomes

   B. one quarter the number of chromosomes

   C. half the number of chromosomes

   D. double the number of chromosomes

12. Sexual reproduction

I.	always produces identical offspring
II.	requires two parents
III.	increases genetic diversity

   A. I and II only

   B. I and III only

   C. II and III only

   D. I, II, and III

13. Meiosis I

   A. starts with a diploid cell and ends with two haploid cells

   B. starts with a haploid cell and ends with two diploid cells

   C. starts with two diploid cells and ends with a haploid cell

   D. starts with a two haploid cells and ends with a diploid cell

14. Meiosis II

   A. starts with two haploid cells and ends with four haploid cells

   B. starts with two diploid cells and ends with four haploid cells

   C. starts with four diploid cells and ends with two haploid cells

   D. starts with four haploid cells and ends with two haploid cells

Sexual Reproduction

Textbook pages 204–223

Before You Read

You began as a zygote. How many cells were you made up of then? How many cells are you made up of now? Record your ideas on the lines below.

_____

_____

Create a Quiz

After you have read this section, create a five-question quiz based on what you have learned. After you have written the questions, be sure to answer them. Then share them with your classmates.

✔ Reading Check

1. When does embryonic development take place?

_____

_____

_____

What is the difference between external and internal fertilization?

Mating is the means by which gametes (sperm and egg cells) meet in the same place at the same time. Mating enables fertilization to take place. Recall that fertilization is the joining of a haploid sperm cell with a haploid egg cell to form a diploid zygote.

When sperm and egg cells join outside of the bodies of the parents, the joining is called **external fertilization**. This type of fertilization is common with animals that live in water and with plants that live in moist places.

When sperm and egg cells join inside the body of the female parent, the joining is called **internal fertilization**. This type of fertilization is common with birds, mammals, and flowering and cone-forming plants.

How does the embryo develop?

Embryonic development takes place during the first eight weeks after fertilization. During this time, the embryo develops. Its cells divide constantly, and tissues and organs form. During the first week, the single fertilized cell, the zygote, develops into a mass of many cells. This mass of cells then hollows out and is called a **blastula**. The cells of the blastula are embryonic stem cells. All tissues and organs will develop from these cells. ✔

During the second week, the blastula cells become organized into three distinct layers of cells. The outer layer is called the ectoderm. The middle layer is called the mesoderm. The inner layer is called the endoderm. The illustration on the next page shows which organs and body structures are formed from the cells of these layers. The development of organs and body structures from these cell layers is called **differentiation**.

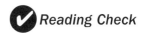

What happens during fetal development?

After the first eight weeks of development, the embryo is called a fetus. During fetal development, the organs and parts of the body continue to develop. The body adds a great deal of mass. At birth, the human baby is made up of trillions of cells. The table below summarizes some key events in fetal development. ✔

Trimester (Group of 3 Months)	Stage	Time from Fertilization	Length of Embryo/ Fetus
First	◆ Brain and spinal cord are forming.	4 weeks	4 mm
	◆ Fingers and toes have appeared. Ears, kidneys, lungs, liver, and muscles are developing.	8 weeks	4 cm
	◆ Sexual differentiation almost complete.	12 weeks	9 cm
Second	◆ Fetal movements are felt.	16–18 weeks	20 cm
	◆ Eyelids open. Fetus can survive outside of the mother with specialized care.	24 weeks	35 cm
Third	◆ Rapid weight gain occurs due to the growth and accumulation of fat.	26–38 weeks	40–50 cm

✔ **Reading Check**

2. What happens during fetal development?

_____

_____

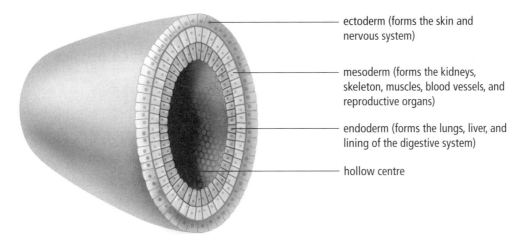

ectoderm (forms the skin and nervous system)

mesoderm (forms the kidneys, skeleton, muscles, blood vessels, and reproductive organs)

endoderm (forms the lungs, liver, and lining of the digestive system)

hollow centre

Blastula cells organize into three layers of cells.

Use with textbook pages 204–220.

Embryonic and fetal development

Vocabulary	
birds	fetus
blastula	fish
differentiation	gametes
ectoderm	internal
embryo	mating
embryonic stem cells	mesoderm
endoderm	offspring
external	

Use the terms in the vocabulary box to fill in the blanks. Use each term only once. You will not need to use every term.

1. _____ is how gametes meet in the same place at the same time.

2. When sperm and egg cells join outside of the bodies of the parents, the joining is called _____ fertilization. This type of fertilization is common with _____.

3. When sperm and egg cells join inside the body of the female parent, the joining is called _____ fertilization. This type of fertilization is common with _____.

4. During embryonic development, the _____ develops. Its cells divide constantly, and tissues and organs form.

5. During the first week, the mass of cells hollows out and is called a(n) _____. Its cells are _____. All tissues and organs will develop from these cells.

6. During the second week, the blastula cells become organized into three distinct layers of cells. The outer layer is called the _____. The middle layer is called the _____. The inner layer is called the _____.

7. The development of organs and body structures from the blastula cell layers is called _____.

8. After the first eight weeks of development, the embryo is called a(n) _____.

Use with textbook pages 206–220.

Types of sexual reproduction

Complete the following table to compare external fertilization with internal fertilization.

	External fertilization	Internal fertilization
Definition		
Draw and label two examples of organisms that use each type of fertilization	1. 2.	1. 2.

Use with textbook pages 216–219.

From human embryo to human baby

Label the diagram and complete the charts below.

Embryonic development	Questions
(a) _____ (b) _____ (c) _____	**1.** Label the three layers of blastula cells on the illustration. **2.** What develops from the ectoderm? _____ _____ **3.** What develops from the mesoderm? _____ _____ _____ **4.** What develops from the endoderm? _____ _____ _____

5. What happens during each of the three trimesters?

Trimester	What is happening at this stage of fetal development?
(a) First	
(b) Second	
(c) Third	

Use with textbook pages 204–220.

Sexual reproduction

Match each Term on the left with the best Descriptor on the right. Each Descriptor may be used only once.	
Term	**Descriptor**
1. _____ differentiation 2. _____ embryonic development 3. _____ external fertilization 4. _____ internal fertilization 5. _____ mating	**A.** development during first eight weeks **B.** development after first eight weeks **C.** the process by which gametes arrive in the same place at the same time **D.** sperm cell and egg cell meet within the female **E.** development of organs and body structures from blastula **F.** sperm cell and egg cell meet outside the bodies of the parents

Circle the letter of the best answer.

6. Which of the following is true of how many flowering plants reproduce?

I.	internal fertilization
II.	external fertilization
III.	sperm and egg cell meet inside the female
IV.	sperm and egg cell meet outside the female

  A. I and III

  B. I and IV

  C. II and III

  D. II and IV

7. In a fetus, the brain and spinal cord are starting to form at

  A. two weeks

  B. four weeks

  C. eight weeks

  D. twelve weeks

8. Fetal movements are felt at

  A. four weeks

  B. eight weeks

  C. twelve weeks

  D. sixteen weeks

Use the following chart to answer questions 9 and 10.

I.	the first and second month after fertilization
II.	the third and fourth month after fertilization
III.	the fifth and sixth month after fertilization
IV.	the seventh and eighth month after fertilization

9. Embryonic development occurs during

  A. I only

  B. I and II only

  C. I, II, and III only

  D. I, II, III, and IV

10. Fetal development occurs during

  A. I only

  B. II and III only

  C. II, III, and IV only

  D. I, II, III, and IV

Assisted Reproductive Technologies

Textbook pages 224–231

Before You Read

What do you think the phrase "test-tube baby" refers to? Write your ideas on the lines below.

_____

_____

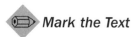 **Mark the Text**

Check for Understanding

As you read this section, be sure to reread any parts you do not understand. Highlight any sentence that helps you develop your understanding.

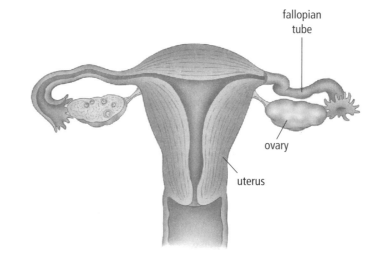

fallopian
tube

ovary

uterus

✔ **Reading Check**

1. What does it mean if a man or a woman is infertile?

_____

_____

What are assisted reproductive technologies?

In some cases, the male or female in a couple (or both) may be infertile—unable to have a child. Assisted reproductive technologies are methods that are used to help infertile couples have a child. Most of these methods include removing egg cells from a woman's body, fertilizing them, and then placing one or more of the embryos in her uterus. ✔

What types of assisted reproductive technologies are there?

Some examples of assisted reproductive technologies are listed in the table on the next page.

Type of technology	How it works
artificial insemination (AI)	Sperm are collected from the male and then injected into the female.
in vitro fertilization (IVF)	A woman's egg cell is placed in a petri dish, and then sperm are injected into the dish so that one sperm cell may fertilize the egg.
gamete intrafallopian transfer (GIFT)	A woman's egg cell is mixed with sperm, and then the mixture is injected into the woman's fallopian tubes. This way, an egg may be fertilized inside the woman's body.
intracytoplasmic sperm injection (ICSI)	A single sperm cell is injected into an egg cell. The fertilized egg is then inserted into the woman's uterus. ✔

How does society respond to these technologies?

Reproductive technologies have helped many couples have a child. However, these methods also raise questions. For instance:

◆ What to do with unused embryos: Not all the embryos that result from these methods are used. What should be done with the unused embryos? Some people want to use them for research purposes. For example, the embryos are a source of stem cells that could be used to help cure diseases or regrow impaired or lost organs. Other people think that it is wrong to use the embryos this way.

◆ Unknown donors: Sperm used in AI are often donated by strangers. Does a child of an AI method have the right to know the identity of his or her biological father?

◆ Surrogate mothers: Sometimes an infertile couple contracts another woman to carry a baby for them. Using AI or IVF, one or both gametes may be provided by the contracting couple. What if the surrogate mother decides she wants to break the contract and keep the baby?

Questions such as these do not have easy answers.

Reading Check

2. In which reproductive technologies does fertilization occur outside the woman's body?

_____
_____
_____

Use with textbook pages 224–229.

Types of assisted reproductive technologies

Vocabulary	
artificial insemination	infertility
assisted reproductive technologies	intracytoplasmic sperm injection
embryos	sperm
fallopian tubes	stem cells
gamete intrafallopian transfer	surrogate mother
gametes	uterus
in vitro fertilization	

Use the terms in the vocabulary box to fill in the blanks. You can use each term more than once. You will not need to use every term.

1. _____ is the inability of a couple to have a baby.

2. Most _____ include removing egg cells from a woman's body, fertilizing them, and placing one or more embryos in the uterus.

3. The _____ is the organ in a female mammal, such as a human, in which an embryo develops and is nourished before birth.

4. Techniques for collecting _____ from a male and injecting it into a female were first developed for animals more than 200 years ago.

5. _____ is a very specialized procedure in which a single sperm cell is injected into an egg cell. The fertilized egg is then injected into the mother's _____.

6. In _____, egg cells are removed from a woman's ovaries and combined with sperm cells. The mixture of eggs and sperm is then injected into the mother's _____ so an egg cell may be fertilized.

7. Sometimes, one or both _____ may be provided so a _____ can become pregnant and give birth to a child for someone else to raise.

8. In _____, a woman's egg cell is placed in a petri dish, and then sperm are injected into the dish.

9. Embryos are a source of _____ that could be used to help cure diseases or regrow impaired or lost organs.

Use with textbook pages 224–228.

Describing assisted reproductive technologies

Complete the following table, describing the different methods of assisted reproductive technologies.

Assisted reproductive technology	Description
1. artificial insemination (AI)	
2. in vitro fertilization (IVF)	
3. gamete intrafallopian transfer (GIFT)	
4. intracytoplasmic sperm injection (ICSI)	

Use with textbook page 229.

Reproductive technologies and society

Find a partner with whom you can discuss the following concerns and questions related to reproductive technologies. Summarize your discussions in the boxes below.

1. Should we continue to use technology that increases the risk of birth defects?	**2.** In the IVF process, extra embryos are produced. What should be done with them?
3. In artificial insemination, the sperm donor is unknown. Should children know the identity of the donor?	**4.** What should happen when a surrogate mother changes her mind and wants to keep the child?

5. What is another question about assisted reproductive technologies that you think needs discussion? _____

_____

_____

Use with textbook pages 224–230.

Assisted reproductive technologies

Match each Term on the left with the best Descriptor on the right. Each Descriptor may be used only once.

Term	Descriptor
1. _____ artificial insemination	A. specialized procedure in which a single sperm is injected into an egg cell
2. _____ assisted reproductive technologies	B. is the inability of a couple to have a baby
3. _____ gamete intrafallopian transfer	C. becomes pregnant and gives birth to a child for someone else to raise
4. _____ in vitro fertilization	D. technologies used to achieve fertilization and pregnancy
5. _____ infertility	E. involves collecting sperm from a male and injecting it into a female
6. _____ intracytoplasmic sperm injection	F. egg cell is mixed with sperm and injected into fallopian tubes
7. _____ surrogate mother	G. procedure to treat specific fertility problems by fertilizing an egg cell in a petri dish
	H. ability of a couple to have a baby

Circle the letter of the best answer.

8. The uterus is where
   A. eggs are produced
   B. sperm are produced
   C. eggs travel along
   D. embryos develop

9. Gamete intrafallopian transfer (GIFT) differs from intracytoplasmic sperm injection (ICSI) because in GIFT an embryo is formed
   A. before it is inserted in the woman's body
   B. naturally with no assisted reproductive technology methods
   C. from a mixture of egg and sperm injected into fallopian tubes
   D. from a mixture of egg and sperm put into a petri dish

10. Artificial insemination (AI) differs from in vitro fertilization (IVF) because in AI
   A. sperm is injected into a female
   B. a mixture of egg and sperm are put in a petri dish
   C. a mixture of egg and sperm is injected into the woman's body
   D. a sperm and egg mixture is placed into the fallopian tubes

11. Questions have been raised about assisted reproductive technologies because

I.	they are naturally occurring
II.	they have helped many couples to have a baby
III.	not everyone agrees about what to do with the unused embryos
IV.	they may increase the risk of birth defects

   A. I and II
   B. I and III
   C. II and III
   D. III and IV

Static Charge

Textbook pages 248–257

Before You Read

Why do you get a shock when you walk across a carpet in wool socks and then touch a metal door handle? Record your thoughts on the lines below.

_____

_____

 **Mark the Text**

Identify Concepts

Highlight each question head in this section. Then use a different colour to highlight the answers to the questions.

What is static charge?

When materials are rubbed together, you might see them cling to each other or move away from each other. Materials that behave in this way are said to carry an electric charge. When a charge stays in place for some length of time, it is described as static electricity or **static charge**.

Why does rubbing make materials charged?

Recall that all matter is made up of atoms. Most of the mass of an atom is in its nucleus—its central core region. The nucleus is made up of two types of particles. Protons are particles that have a positive (+) charge. Neutrons are particles that do not have a charge so they are neutral. The space around the nucleus contains fast-moving particles called electrons. Electrons have a negative (−) charge.

The overall charge of a material depends on the balance between the positive and negative charges in all the atoms of the material. A material may be neutral, have a positive charge, or have a negative charge.

When two materials are rubbed, electrons from the atoms of one material may move to the atoms of the other material. The movement of electrons from one atom to another changes the charge on the atoms. When an atom loses electrons, it is left with more protons than electrons, so its charge is positive. When an atom gains electrons, it has more electrons than protons, so its charge is negative. ✔

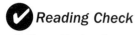 **Reading Check**

1. Name the two types of charged particles in an atom.

_____

_____

Name _____

Date _____

Section
7.1
Summary

continued

Charges in a material that is neutral (uncharged)	Charges in a material that is positively charged	Charges in a material that is negatively charged
+ + − + − − − − + − + +	+ + + + + − − − + + + +	− − − + − + − − − + − +
equal protons and electrons	more protons than electrons	more electrons than protons

How else can charges be produced?

You already know that charges can be produced by rubbing (friction). This can happen in nature when air rubs against ice crystals and dust particles in clouds, producing lightning. Scientists also use a friction-producing machine called a **Van de Graaff generator** to create charges that they can study.

How easily do charges move in different materials?

Electrons cannot move easily in materials such as **acetate** (a type of plastic), rubber, wool, and glass. Materials that do not let electrons move through them easily are called **insulators**. Charges tend to build up on insulators.

    Electrons can move easily through materials such as metals. Materials that let electrons move through them easily are called **conductors**. Sometimes, a conductor is used to transfer static charges from an object to the ground. Allowing charge to flow into Earth's surface is called **grounding**. ✔

How are charges measured?

Electric charges are measured in units called **coulombs** (C). A bright light bulb, for example, allows about 1 C (one coulomb) of electric charge to pass through it each second.

Charges on insulator

Charges on conductor

Reading Check

2. What does a conductor allow to move easily through it?

_____

_____

Use with textbook pages 248–254.

Charge it

Vocabulary	
acetate	negative
atoms	neutral
conductors	neutrons
coulomb	nucleus
electric	positive
electrons	protons
grounding	static charge
insulators	Van de Graaff generator

Use the terms in the vocabulary box to fill in the blanks. You may use terms more than once. You will not need to use every term.

1. Static electricity is also known as ____static charge ✓____.
   This refers to the build-up of electric charge in one place.

2. All matter is made of tiny particles called ~~electrons~~ atoms ____.

3. The positively charged ____nucleus ✓____ is the centre of the atom.
   It consists of positively charged subatomic particles called ____Protons ✓____
   and subatomic particles with no charge called ____neutrons ✓____ ~~neutrons~~ ~~neutral~~.

4. The negatively charged subatomic particles called ____electrons ✓____ ~~neu~~ ~~neutrons~~
   occupy the area around the nucleus.

5. An object is uncharged or ____neutral ✓____ when the number of
   positive charges equals the number of negative charges.

6. If an atom loses an electron, it has more protons than electrons. This atom will have
   an overall ____~~nutral~~ positive____ charge.

7. If an atom gains an electron, it has more electrons than protons. This atom will have
   an overall ____~~positive~~ negative____ charge.

8. Glass and acetate are examples of ____~~coulomb~~ insulators____ because they
   do not allow electrons to move easily through them. Metals like copper and aluminum
   are good ____conductors____ because they allow electrons
   to move freely through them.

9. The ____insulator coulomb____ is a unit of electric charge.

10. Scientists use a(n) ____~~insulator~~ Van de Graaff ✓ generator____ to create static charge.

11. Lightning rods on top of buildings allow static charges from lightning to flow into
    Earth's surface. This is known as ____grounding ✓____.

Use with textbook pages 248–254.

Static charge detective

Use the following diagram to answer the questions.

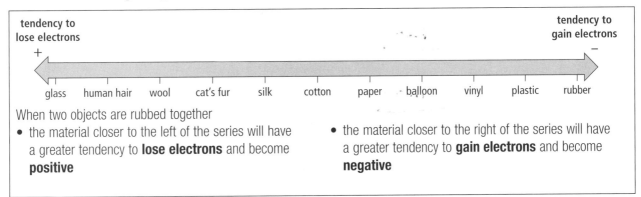

tendency to lose electrons
tendency to gain electrons

+ 　　　　　　　　　　　　　　　　　　　　　　　　　　　　　　 −

glass　human hair　wool　cat's fur　silk　cotton　paper　balloon　vinyl　plastic　rubber

When two objects are rubbed together
- the material closer to the left of the series will have a greater tendency to **lose electrons** and become **positive**
- the material closer to the right of the series will have a greater tendency to **gain electrons** and become **negative**

1. As you take your clothes out of the dryer, your wool socks are clinging to your silk skirt. What is the charge on the wool socks and on the silk skirt?

Charge on socks

positive ✓

Charge on skirt

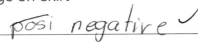
posi negative ✓

2. You use a plastic comb to comb your hair. What is the charge on your hair and on the comb?

Charge on comb

positive

Charge on hair

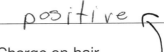
negative ✓

3. You use a paper towel to rub off some dirt on a glass window. What is the charge on the glass and on the paper towel?

Charge on window

positive ✓

Charge on paper towel

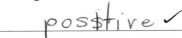
negative ✓

4. You rub a balloon along your cat's back, causing the cat's fur to stand up. What is the charge on the balloon and on the cat's fur?

Charge on balloon

po negative ✓

Charge on cat's fur

positive ✓

Use with textbook pages 248–254.

Conductors and insulators

Define and identify conductors and insulators as directed below.

1. Define the following terms.

   (a) conductor _an **object** (fabric) that alows electrons to move freely with in it_

   (b) insulator _an **object** (fabric) that dosent let electrons move freely between them_

2. On the first line, indicate whether the object is a conductor or an insulator. On the second line, state whether or not the material allows electrons to move freely.

(a)

insulator
_no_

(b)
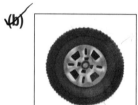
insulator
_no_

(c)

conductor
yes

(d)

conductor
yes

(e)

conductor
yes

(f)

insulator
_no_

Use with textbook pages 248–254.

Static charge

Match each Term on the left with the corresponding Diagram label on the right. Each label may be used more than once.	
Term	**Diagram**
1. _c_ proton	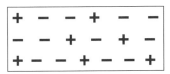
2. _b_ neutron	
3. _a_ electron	
4. _B_ has no charge	
5. _c_ has a positive charge	
6. _a_ has a negative charge	
7. _a_ can move from one atom to another	
8. _B_ and _c_ make up the nucleus (name 2 parts of the atom) *protons neutron*	

Circle the letter of the best answer.

9. A neutral object has exactly the same number of

   (A) protons and neutrons

   (B) protons and electrons

   C. neutrons and electrons

   D. protons, neutrons, and electrons

Use the following diagram to answer question 10.

```
+ – + – + – + –
– + – + – + – +
+ – + – + – + –
```

10. What is the electric charge on the object shown above?

   (A) neutral

   B. positive

   C. negative

   D. It is impossible to tell.

Use the following diagram to answer questions 11 and 12.

```
+ – – + – –
– – + – + –
+ – – + – – +
```

11. What is the electric charge on the object shown above?

   A. neutral

   B. positive

   (C.) negative

   D. It is impossible to tell.

12. Which of the following describes the object shown above?

   A. It lost protons.

   B. It lost electrons.

   C. It gained protons.

   (D.) It gained electrons.

13. A vinyl rod is rubbed with a cotton cloth. The vinyl rod becomes negatively charged and the cotton cloth becomes positively charged. Which of the following describes the cotton cloth?

   A. It has gained electrons.

   B. It has more electrons than protons.

   (C.) It has more protons than electrons.

   D. It has the same number of protons as electrons.

14. Which of the following is a good conductor?

   A. glass

   B. wood

   (C.) copper

   D. fur

Electric Force

Textbook pages 258–265

Before You Read

If you rub a balloon on a sweater it will stick to the wall. Why? Write your ideas on the lines below.

_____

_____

Make Flash Cards

For each paragraph, think of a question that might be on a test. Then write the question on one side of a flash card. Write the answer on the other side. Quiz yourself until you can answer all the questions.

✔ **Reading Check**

1. What will happen if a pen with a positive charge comes near paper with a negative charge?

_____

_____

_____

_____

What laws describe electric charges?

Electric force is a pull (attraction) or a push (repulsion) between objects that are charged. The **laws of static charge** describe what happens when charged and uncharged objects come close to each other.

The Laws of Static Charge

1. Objects with the same charge repel each other.
2. Objects with opposite charges attract each other.
3. Charged objects attract neutral objects. ✔

The electric force that acts on any pair of objects depends on:

◆ the type of charge on the objects (positive, negative, or neutral)
◆ the amount of charge on the objects
◆ the distance between the objects

If you increase the amount of charge on objects, you increase the electric force. If you increase the distance between objects, you decrease the electric force.

What is an electroscope?

An electroscope is a device that can be used to detect the presence of charge. A typical electroscope has one or two lightweight strips of metal that bend easily. These metal strips, called leaves, are attached to a central metal rod that has a metal sphere at the top. Sometimes, the leaves and metal rod are enclosed in glass or plastic so that air movement does not affect the device. When the leaves repel each other, you know they are charged.

What is charging by conduction?

When you charge a neutral object by touching it to a charged object, it is called **charging by conduction**. For example, if you touch a neutral electroscope with a negatively charged rod, electrons are added to the electroscope and spread over the surface of the metal leaves. The leaves then become negatively charged and repel each other.

What is charging by induction?

You do not have to touch the sphere of an electroscope to make the leaves separate. If you bring a negatively charged rod near—but not touching—the sphere, the rod will repel the electrons in the sphere. The negative charges will move down to the leaves and the leaves will repel each other. This is called **charging by induction**. The sphere will be left with a temporary positive charge. If the negatively charged rod is removed, the electrons will move back to the sphere, and the sphere will be neutral again. ✔

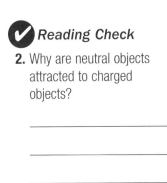

Reading Check

2. Why are neutral objects attracted to charged objects?

_____

_____

_____

Why are neutral objects attracted to charged objects?

Neutral objects are attracted to charged objects because the neutral objects are temporarily charged by induction. For example, a negatively charged balloon sticks to a neutral wall because the balloon's negative charges repel the wall's negative charges. In other words, a positive charge is induced on the surface of the wall. The negative balloon is attracted to the positive wall surface.

Charging an electroscope by conduction

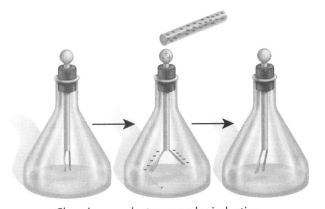

Charging an electroscope by induction

Use with textbook pages 258–262.

Neutral, positive, or negative charges?

Answer the questions below in the spaces provided.

1. What are the three laws of static charge?

   (a) opposites attract

   (b) like repel

   (c) neutral attract to charged objects

2. For each situation illustrated below, will the objects shown attract or repel each other?

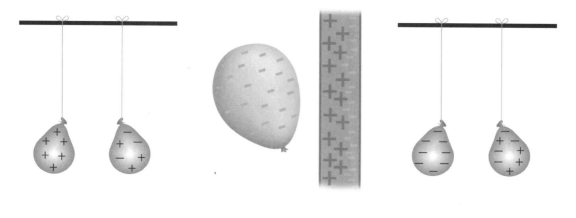

(a) attract   (b) attract   (c) attract

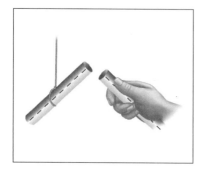 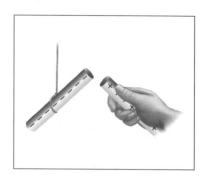

(d) repel   (e) repel   (f) attracts

Use with textbook pages 258–262.

Charging by conduction or induction

Analyze the situations below. Do they describe charging by conduction or induction?

1. Identify whether the situation is describing charging by conduction or induction.

   (a) You notice the build-up of dust on a computer screen when it is on.
   induction

   (b) You walk across a carpet and experience a shock when you touch a metal doorknob. _conduction_

   (c) You rub a balloon against your hair and bring it close to a pile of salt on the table. This causes the salt crystals to "jump up and dance." _induction_

2. Identify whether the illustration shows charging by conduction or induction.

   (a)

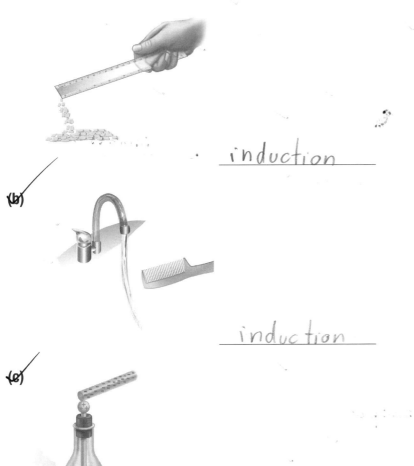

induction

   (b)

induction

   (c)

conduction

Use with textbook pages 258–262.

Positive, negative, and neutral objects

Vocabulary	
amount of charge	electroscope
attract	increase
conduction	induction
contact forces	laws of static charge
decrease	neutral
distance between objects	repel
electric force	type of charge

Use the terms in the vocabulary box to fill in the blanks. Each term may be used more than once. You will not need to use every term.

1. A(n) _electric force_ is a push or pull between charged objects.

2. The _laws of static charge_ state that like charges _repel_ and opposite charges _attract_. Charged objects are attracted to _neutral_ objects.

3. The electric force that acts on any pair of objects depends on the _distance between objects_ and _type of charge_ on the objects and on the _amount of charge_.

4. If you increase the amount of charge on objects, you _~~decrease~~ increase_ the electric force. If you _increase_ the distance between objects, you decrease the electric force.

5. A device that can detect the presence of charge is the _electroscope_.

6. If the leaves of an electroscope become charged, they will _repel_ each other.

7. If a charged rod is brought close to an electroscope and then removed, the electroscope will become _neutral_.

8. Charging by _conduction_ occurs when objects touch and an electric charge is transferred from one object to the other. A(n) _electroscope_ can be used to demonstrate this.

9. Charging by _induction_ occurs when objects are charged without touching. A(n) _electroscope_ can be used to demonstrate this.

10. Neutral objects are attracted to charged objects because they are charged by _~~electric force~~ induction_

Use with textbook pages 258–262.

Electric force

Match each Diagram on the left with the best Descriptor on the right. Each Descriptor may be used more than once.

Diagram	Descriptor
1. *A* _____	**A.** suspended spheres will move away from each other
2. *B* _____	**B.** suspended spheres will move toward each other
3. *B* _____	**C.** suspended spheres will not move
4. *a* _____	

Circle the letter of the best answer.

5. Which of the following applies to a neutral object?

I.	It is attracted to a positive surface.
II.	It is attracted to a negative surface.
III.	It has the same number of protons as electrons.

A. I and II only

B. I and III only

C. II and III only

D. I, II, and III

6. A negatively charged ruler is brought near a suspended ball. The ball is repelled by the ruler. What can you conclude from this observation?

A. The ball is neutral.

B. The ball is positively charged.

C. The ball is negatively charged.

D. The ball is either neutral or positively charged.

7. Two suspended balloons repel each other when brought close together. What can you conclude about the balloons?

A. They have opposite charges.

B. They both have the same charge.

C. One balloon is neutral and the other balloon is positively charged.

D. One balloon is neutral and the other balloon is negatively charged.

8. How does the electric force change as the amount of charge is increased?

A. It increases.

B. It decreases.

C. It stays the same.

D. It increases and then decreases.

9. Which of the following statements is true about the relationship between distance and electric force?

A. If the distance between charged objects decreases, the electric force decreases.

B. If the distance between charged objects decreases, the electric force stays the same.

C. If the distance between charged objects increases, the electric force increases.

D. If the distance between charged objects increases, the electric force decreases.

Electric Potential Energy and Voltage

Textbook pages 270–279

Before You Read

Static electricity involves charges that build up and stay in the same place on an object. How could you store the charges to use later? Write down your ideas on the lines below.

_____

_____

Mark the Text

Identify Definitions

As you read this section, highlight the definition of each word that appears in bold type.

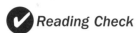

Reading Check

1. What is electric potential energy?

_____

_____

_____

What is a battery?

Energy is the ability to do work—to make things move or change. A **battery** is a device that stores the energy in electric charges so that it can be used at some later time to do work. In other words, a battery is a source of **electric potential energy**—stored energy that has the potential to make something move or change.

Batteries convert chemical energy to electrical energy. For example, batteries that power a flashlight or a cordless mouse convert chemical energy to electrical energy. Batteries that convert chemical energy to electrical energy are called **electrochemical cells**, and may be wet cells or dry cells (see illustration). ✅

How does a battery provide energy?

A battery provides energy to push negative charges through conductors that are connected together. Energy to push electrons is available if positive and negative charges are separated. In a flashlight battery, for example, energy from chemical reactions does the work of separating the charges.

A flashlight battery has two terminals called **electrodes** in a moist paste called an **electrolyte** that conducts electricity. Electrons build up at one terminal, making it negatively charged. At the same time, electrons withdraw from the other terminal, leaving it positively charged. Once the charges are separated, the charges have the ability to do work on something else, such as making a bulb light up.

Electric Potential Energy and Voltage

What is voltage?

Scientists use the term **potential difference** to talk about the difference in potential energy per coulomb of charge between two points of an electric circuit. Potential difference is another name for **voltage**. The standard unit for voltage is the **volt** (V). The label 1.5 V on a battery means that it has a potential difference of 1.5 V. Voltage can be measured by a **voltmeter**.

Voltage is what causes charges to move. Think of a waterfall. The water in a waterfall naturally flows from a higher point to a lower point. In a similar way, charges naturally move from a higher level of energy to a lower level of energy. The difference in potential energy between one point in a circuit and another—the voltage—makes charges move in a circuit. ✔

✔ *Reading Check*

2. What is another name for voltage?

_____

_____

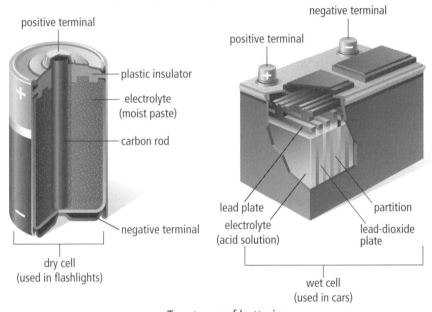

positive terminal

plastic insulator

electrolyte (moist paste)

carbon rod

negative terminal

dry cell (used in flashlights)

negative terminal

positive terminal

lead plate

electrolyte (acid solution)

partition

lead-dioxide plate

wet cell (used in cars)

Two types of batteries

Use with textbook pages 270–275.

Electricity crossword puzzle

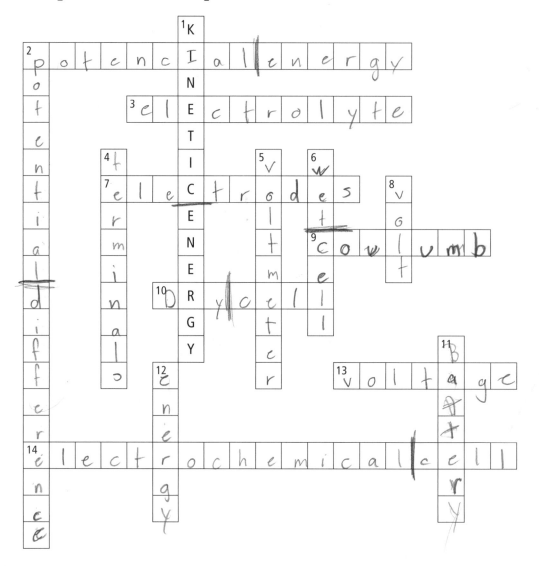

Across	Down
2. stored energy *Potencial energy*	1. energy a moving object has *kinetic energy*
3. electrodes are placed in a substance that conducts electricity *electrolyte*	2. another name for voltage *potencial difference*
7. two terminals in a battery *electrodes*	4. positive and negative end points of a battery *terminal*
9. unit for charge *Coulumb*	5. device used to measure voltage *voltmeter*
10. battery in flashlights *Dry cell*	6. battery in cars *wet cell*
13. amount of electric potential energy per one coulomb of charge *Voltage*	8. unit for potential difference *volt*
14. converts chemical energy into electrical energy *electrochemical cell*	11. converts a form of energy into electrical energy *Battery*
	12. ability to do work *energy*

Name _Cassie Berg_   Date _____

Use with textbook pages 270–275.

Electric potential energy

Vocabulary	
~~battery~~	positively
~~chemical~~	~~potential difference~~
~~electrical~~	potential energy
electrochemical cell	removed
~~electrodes~~	~~separated~~
~~electrolyte~~	terminals
~~energy~~	volt
negatively	voltage

Use the terms in the vocabulary box to fill in the blanks. You may use terms more than once. You will not need to use every term.

1. The ability to do work is called ___energy✓___.

2. A device that stores the energy in electric charges so that it can be used at some later time to do work is called a(n) ___battery✓___ or ~~potential energy~~ _elecrochemical cell_

3. Energy that is stored in a battery is called electric ~~charge~~ _potential energy_

4. A battery that powers a flashlight converts ___chemical✓___ energy to ___electrical✓___ energy.

5. Energy to push electrons is available if positive and negative charges are ___separated✓___.

6. In a flashlight battery, energy from ___chemical___ reactions does the work of separating the charges.

7. A flashlight battery has two terminals called ___electrodes✓___ in a moist paste called a(n) ___electrolyte✓___.

8. Electrons build up at one terminal, making it ___negatively✓___ charged. At the same time, electrons withdraw from the other terminal, leaving it ___positively✓___ charged.

9. ___potential difference✓___, or voltage, is the difference in energy per coulomb of charge between one point in a circuit and another point in a circuit.

Use with textbook pages 270–275.

Electrochemical cells

**Use the following terms to label the two diagrams. You can use terms more than once.
Some parts have been labelled for you.**

Terms	
carbon rod	negative terminal
electrolyte	plastic insulator
lead plate	positive terminal

1.

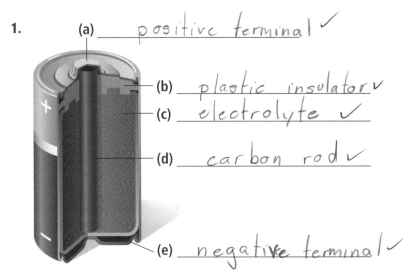

(a) _positive terminal_ ✓

(b) _plastic insulator_ ✓

(c) _electrolyte_ ✓

(d) _carbon rod_ ✓

(e) _negative terminal_ ✓

2.

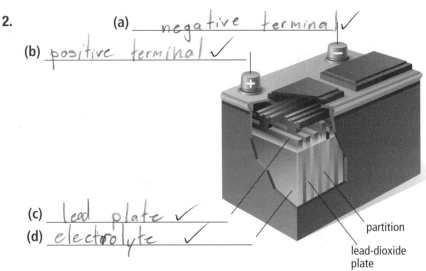

(a) _negative terminal_ ✓

(b) _positive terminal_ ✓

(c) _lead plate_ ✓

(d) _electrolyte_ ✓

partition

lead-dioxide
plate

Use with textbook pages 270–275.

Electric potential energy and voltage

Match each Term on the left with the best Descriptor on the right. Each Descriptor may be used only once.	
Term	**Descriptor**
1. _C_ electrochemical cell 2. _F_ potential energy 3. _D_ potential difference 4. _a_ electrode 5. _B_ electrolyte	**A.** battery terminal **B.** conducts electricity **C.** converts chemical energy into electrical energy **D.** another name for voltage **E.** energy from motion **F.** stored energy

Circle the letter of the best answer.

6. Which of the following could be used to measure the amount of potential difference in a circuit?

   A. electrode

   B. voltmeter

   C. electrolyte

   D. electroscope

7. What is the unit for measuring potential difference?

   A. volt (V)

   B. second (s)

   C. metre (m)

   D. coulomb (C)

Use the following diagram to answer questions 8 and 9.

8. What is shown in the diagram above?

   A. dry cell

   B. wet cell

   C. voltmeter

   D. electroscope

9. Which of the following describes the electrolyte used in the object shown above?

   A. a fluid

   B. a moist paste

   C. an acid solution

   D. a copper electrode

10. Which of the following are different names for the same thing?

I.	battery
II.	electrochemical cell
III.	electric potential difference

   A. I and II only

   B. I and III only

   C. II and III only

   D. I, II, and III

Electric Current

Textbook pages 280–289

Before You Read

What is needed for a light bulb to light up? Write your ideas on the lines below.

_____

_____

 *Mark the Text*

Check for Understanding

As you read this section, be sure to reread any parts you do not understand. Highlight any sentences that help you develop your understanding.

✓ Reading Check

1. What is an electric circuit?

_____

_____

_____

✓ Reading Check

2. What is the name of the device used to measure electric current?

_____

What is needed for charges to move through an electric circuit?

A continuous movement of charge through a conductor is called **current electricity**. A complete pathway through which electrons can flow is called an **electric circuit**. An electric circuit has the following basic parts:

◆ There must be a *source* of electrical energy. This may be a battery or a wall outlet.

◆ There must be a *conductor* through which charges can move. This is usually a metal wire.

◆ There must be a device, called a *load*, which converts electrical energy into other forms of energy such as light or sound. Light bulbs, speakers, heaters, and motors are examples of loads.

◆ There may be a *switch*—a device that can control the movement of charges in the circuit by turning it on (closing the circuit) or turning it off (opening the circuit). ✓

What is electric current and how is it measured?

An electrical source such as a battery provides energy to push negative charges through the conducting wires in a circuit. This movement of charge is called *current*. **Electric current** is the amount of charge that passes a point in a conducting wire each second.

Electric current is measured in units called **amperes** (A). A current of one ampere (1.0 A) is produced when 1.0 C (coulombs) of charged particles move past a point in a circuit each second. Electric current is measured with a device called an **ammeter**. ✓

What does an electric circuit look like?

The parts of a circuit can be drawn with symbols to show how the circuit is connected. A picture that is made using these symbols to represent an actual circuit is called a **circuit diagram**.

Examples of symbols used in circuit diagrams:

————	conducting wire	—(ᴍ)—	bulb
+ − ⊣⊢	cell	—/ •—	open switch
+ − ⊣⎮⎮⊢	battery	—•—•—	closed switch
—(V)—	voltmeter	—(A)—	ammeter

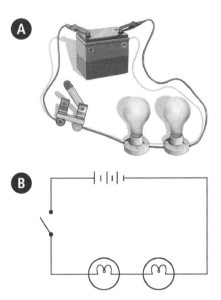

A

B

This circuit diagram (B) shows the parts of the circuit (A).
Find each of the objects from circuit A in circuit B.

Use with textbook pages 280–285.

Identifying circuit symbols

Match the Term in the first column with the correct Illustration and Circuit Symbol in the other two columns. Place the corresponding letter and Roman numeral in the blank spaces provided.

Term	Illustration	Circuit Symbol

1. bulb
   C IV
  _____
	A.	**I.** ___•_•___

2. battery
   B V
  _____
	B.	**II.** __•_/_•__

3. open switch
   D II
  _____
	C.	**III.** _____

4. closed switch
   C- I
  _____
	D.	**IV.**

5. conducting wire
   A III
  _____
	E.	**V.**

List all the parts in the following electrical circuit.

6.

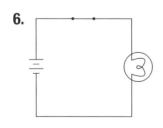

Battery, Bulb, conducting wire and closed switch

Use with textbook pages 280–285.

Drawing circuit diagrams

Use circuit symbols to draw circuit diagrams for each of the following.

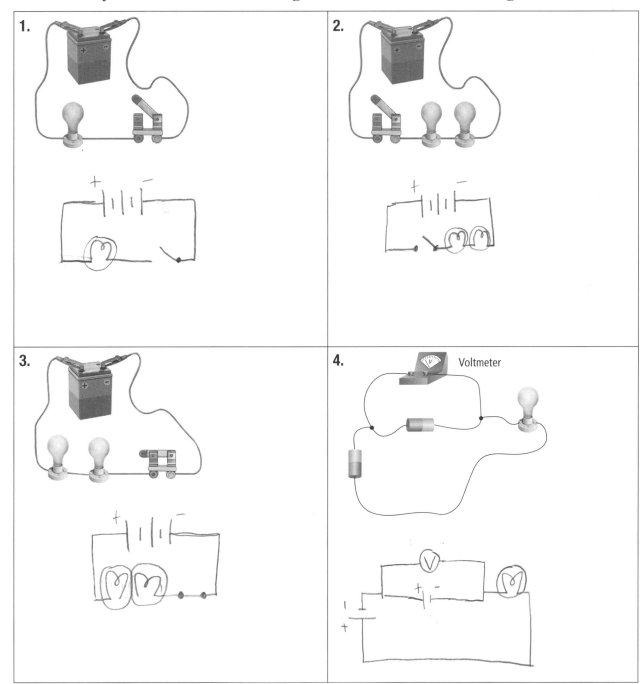

1.

2.

3.

4. Voltmeter

Use with textbook pages 280–285.

True or false?

Read the statements given below. If the statement is true, write "T" on the line in front of the statement. If it is false, write "F" and rewrite the statement to make it true.

1. __T__ An electric circuit is a complete pathway through which electrons can flow.

_____

2. __F__ An electric load transforms light energy into electrical energy.

_____

3. __T__ Light bulbs, heaters, and batteries are all examples of electric loads.

_____

4. __T__ The wire through which electric current flows is a conductor.

_____

5. __F__ A switch is the source of electric potential energy in a circuit.

A Battery is the source...

6. __T__ Circuit diagrams use circuit symbols to illustrate actual electrical circuits.

_____

7. __F__ Current electricity is charge that remains stationary on an insulator.

Static electricity

8. __T__ Electric current is the amount of charge passing a point in a conducting wire each second.

_____

_____

9. __F__ Electric current is measured in volts.

measured

10. __T__ An ammeter is used to measure the current in a circuit.

_____

Use with textbook pages 280–285.

Electric current

Match each Term on the left with the letter on the Diagram on the right. Each letter on the Diagram may be used only once.

Term	Diagram
1. _A_ cell	
2. _D_ bulb	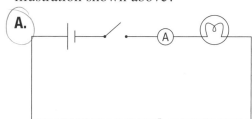
3. _B_ switch	
4. _F_ circuit diagram	
5. _C_ conducting wire	

Circle the letter of the best answer.

6. What does the symbol ——(A)—— represent?

  A. a load

  B. a battery

  C. a voltmeter

  D. an ammeter

7. Which of the following are correctly defined?

I.	ampere: unit for electric current
II.	ammeter: device used to measure current
III.	electric circuit: an incomplete pathway through which electrons can flow

  A. I and II only

  B. I and III only

  C. II and III only

  D. I, II, and III

8. Which of the following is not an example of an electric load?

  A. a motor

  B. a heater

  C. a light bulb

  D. a generator

Use the following diagram to answer question 9.

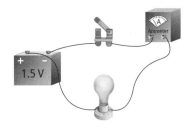

9. Which circuit diagram represents the illustration shown above?

A.

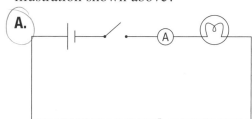

B.

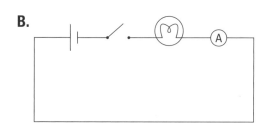

C.

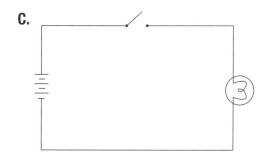

D.

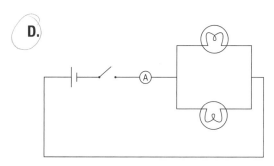

Text pg. 285 #1-8
289 #1,2, 10,12

Resistance and Ohm's Law

Textbook pages 290–301

Before You Read

Do you think electrons can move through all conducting substances equally well? Give your reasons why or why not on the lines below.

_____

_____

Create an Outline

Make an outline of the information in this section. Use the headings in the reading as a starting point. Include the bold terms and any other terms that you think are important.

What is resistance?

Electrical resistance is the property of a substance that slows down the movement of electrons and converts electrical energy into other forms of energy. For instance, the resistance of the tungsten filament in a light bulb is more than 400 times greater than the resistance of copper connecting wires. When current moves through the high-resistance filament of the light bulb, the filament converts much of the energy carried by the current into light and heat. When the same current moves through the copper wire, the amount of energy converted into heat is much smaller.

The unit used for measuring resistance is the **ohm** (Ω). An ohmmeter can be used to measure resistance.

How is resistance related to voltage and current?

Voltage, current, and resistance are closely related.

◆ Current is the movement of electrons (charges) through a conductor.

◆ Voltage is what makes the electrons move through the conductor.

◆ Resistance works against and slows down the motion of the electrons.

Good conductors have low resistance, which means that electrons flow through them easily. Poor conductors have high resistance, which means electrons are slowed down.

How does Ohm's law relate voltage, current, and resistance?

Ohm's law is a mathematical equation that shows how voltage, current, and resistance are related:

$$\text{resistance} = \frac{\text{voltage}}{\text{current}} \text{ or } R = \frac{V}{I},$$

where R stands for resistance, V stands for voltage, and I stands for current.

You can rewrite this equation to solve for any of the variables in it. Thus:

$$\text{voltage} = \text{current} \times \text{resistance } (V = IR); \text{ and}$$

$$\text{current} = \frac{\text{voltage}}{\text{resistance}} \ (I = \frac{V}{R}) \ \checkmark$$

What is a resistor?

A **resistor** is a component in a circuit that has a specific resistance. Resistors are used to control current or voltage to suit the needs of other electric devices in the circuit. The circuit symbol for a resistor looks like this: ———⋀⋀⋀——— ✓

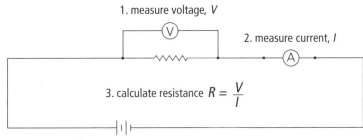

1. measure voltage, V

2. measure current, I

3. calculate resistance $R = \frac{V}{I}$

Using Ohm's law, you can calculate resistance from current and voltage measurements.

✔ *Reading Check*

1. State Ohm's law in words.

_____

_____

_____

✔ *Reading Check*

2. What is a resistor?

_____

_____

_____

Use with textbook pages 290–297.

Voltage, current, and resistance

Follow the directions below to demonstrate what you know about voltage, current, and resistance.

1. Define the following terms.

   (a) current _amount of change passing a point in a conductor every second._

   (b) voltage _amount of electric potential energy per one coulomb of change_

   (c) resistance _opposition to flow of current through a circuit_

   (d) Ohm's law _math equation to show how voltage, current and resistance are related_

   (e) resistor _a component in a circuit that has a specific resistance used to control current / voltage_

2. Complete the following table. The table has been partially completed to help you.

	Current	Voltage	Resistance
Symbol	I / A	V	R
Unit	ampheres	volt	ohm (Ω)
Meter used for measurement	ammeter	voltmeter	ohmmeter
Formula	$I = \dfrac{V}{R}$	$V = I \times R$	$R = \dfrac{V}{I}$

Name _____   Date _____

Use with textbook pages 290–297.

Calculations with Ohm's law

Use Ohm's law to complete the following table. Write the formula you will use and substitute the known values into the formula. Show all your work and include the correct unit with your answer. The first question has been done to help guide you.

	Question	Show your work	Answer
1.	A current through a resistor in a circuit is 1.5 A. If the potential difference across the resistor is 6 V, what is the resistance of the resistor?	$R = V \div I$ $= 6\ V \div 1.5\ A$ $= 4\ \Omega$	$4\ \Omega$
2.	A toaster is plugged into a 120 V outlet. What is the resistance of the toaster if the current in the toaster is 10 A?	$R = \dfrac{V}{I}$ $= \dfrac{120}{10}$ $= 12$	$12\ \Omega$
3.	A light bulb with a resistance of 30 Ω is connected to a battery. If the current in the light bulb is 0.2 A, what is the voltage of the battery?	$V = I \times R$ $= 30 \times 0.2$ $= 6$	$6\ V$
4.	What is the current in a flashlight bulb with a resistance of 24 Ω if the voltage provided by the flashlight battery is 3 V?	$I = \dfrac{V}{R}$ $= \dfrac{3}{24}$ $= 0.125$	$0.125\ A$
5.	An electric iron plugged into a wall socket has a resistance of 20 Ω. If the current in the iron is 6 A, what is the voltage provided by the wall socket?	$V = I \times R$ $= 20\ 6 \times 20$ $= 120$	$120\ V$

Use with textbook pages 290–297.

Relationship between current, voltage, and resistance

Use the graph below to answer the questions that follow.

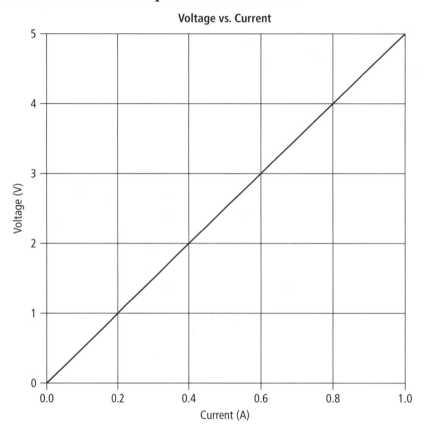

1. (a) What happens to the voltage as the current increases?

as current increases voltage increases

(b) What does this suggest about the relationship between voltage and current?

a positive between voltage and current

2. According to the graph, what happens to the voltage when the current is doubled?

voltage doubles

Use with textbook pages 290–297.

Resistance and Ohm's law

Match the Formula or Unit on the left with the best Descriptor on the right. Each Descriptor may be used only once.	
Formula or Unit	**Descriptor**
1. _E_ $I = V \div R$	**A.** unit for voltage
2. _F_ $R = V \div I$	**B.** unit for current
3. _D_ $V = I \times R$	**C.** unit for resistance
4. _A_ volts (V)	**D.** formula for voltage
5. _C_ ohms (Ω)	**E.** formula for current
6. _B_ amperes (A)	**F.** formula for resistance

Circle the letter of the best answer.

7. Which of the following correctly matches the devices with what they measure?

	Ammeter	**Ohmmeter**	**Voltmeter**
A.	current	voltage	resistance
B.	resistance	current	voltage
C.	voltage	resistance	current
D.	current	resistance	voltage

8. What is the name of the law given to the mathematical relationship between voltage, current, and resistance?

A. Ohm's law

B. Voltage's law

C. Ampere's law

D. Electricity's law

9. Which of the following describes resistance?

I.	It resists the flow of electrons.
II.	It speeds up the current flow in a circuit.
III.	It causes the electron's electrical energy to be converted to heat and light energy.

A. I and II only

B. I and III only

C. II and III only

D. I, II, and III

10. Which of the following occurs if resistance is increased in a circuit?

A. Both voltage and current will increase.

B. Both voltage and current will decrease.

C. Voltage will increase and current will decrease.

D. Voltage will decrease and current will increase.

11. What does the symbol ——⌇⌇⌇—— represent?

A. a load

B. a resistor

C. a voltmeter

D. an ammeter

12. A 6 V battery is connected to a 10 Ω resistor. What is the current flowing in the circuit?

A. 0.6 A

B. 1.67 A

C. 4 A

D. 60 A

Series and Parallel Circuits

Textbook pages 306–319

Before You Read

A circuit is a complete pathway like an electric circuit or a school running track. What other examples of circuits can you list?

_____

_____

 **Mark the Text**

Identify Concepts

As you read, highlight each question head in this section. Then use a different colour to highlight the answers to the questions.

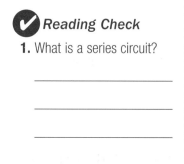 **Reading Check**

1. What is a series circuit?

_____

_____

_____

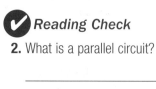 **Reading Check**

2. What is a parallel circuit?

_____

_____

_____

What is a series circuit?

A **series circuit** is an electric circuit that has only one pathway for electric current to take. You can think of a series circuit as a set of parts that are connected end to end. The charges pass through each load before they return to a battery or other energy source. All the moving charges travel through each part of the circuit. ✔

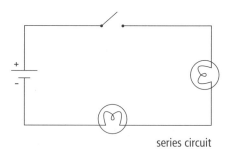

series circuit

What is a parallel circuit?

A **parallel circuit** is an electric circuit that has two or more pathways for electric current to take. Some of the moving charges travel through one pathway of the circuit, and other moving charges travel through other pathways of the circuit. All the charges return to the source after moving through the pathways. The place where pathways separate or join in a parallel circuit is called a **junction point**. ✔

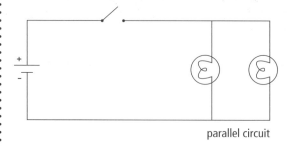

parallel circuit

What happens to the current, voltage, and resistance in series and parallel circuits?

The table below summarizes the effects that series circuits and parallel circuits have on the current, the voltage, and the resistance of the circuits.

Series circuit	Parallel circuit
Current The current through the whole circuit is the same throughout and is equal to the total current supplied by the source.	***Current*** The current through each pathway of the circuit adds up to the total current supplied by the source.
Voltage The voltages across each of the loads in the circuit add up to the voltage supplied by the source.	***Voltage*** The voltages across each of the loads in the circuit are equal to each other and to the voltage supplied by the source.
Resistance Resistors placed in series increase the total resistance of the circuit. As a result, the total current throughout the circuit decreases.	***Resistance*** Resistors placed in parallel decrease the total resistance of the circuit. As a result, the total current through the circuit increases.

Use with textbook pages 306–313.

Series or parallel?

For each of the following statements, identify whether it applies to a series circuit or a parallel circuit.

1. The current is the same throughout the circuit.

   series circuit

2. Adding a resistor will decrease the total resistance of the circuit.

   parallel circuit

3. The voltage across each resistor in the circuit is the same.

   parallel

4. There is only one pathway for electrons to flow.

   series

5. Adding a resistor will increase the total resistance of the circuit.

   series

6. There is more than one pathway for current to flow.

   parallel

7. As more cells are added to the circuit, the brightness of the light bulb increases.

   parallel

8. There are junction points in the circuit.

   parallel

9. If the current through one load in the circuit goes to 0 A, the current through all other loads remains the same.

   series

10. The sum of voltages across the loads equals the total voltage supplied by the battery.

    parallel

11. The total current entering a junction point equals the sum of the current leaving the junction point.

    parallel

Use with textbook pages 306–313.

Is it in series or in parallel?

Match each description on the left with the correct circuit on the right.

Description	Circuit
1. __B__ 3 resistors in series	**A.** ⊚ ③ ③
2. __D__ 3 resistors in parallel	**B.**
3. __E__ 2 light bulbs in series	**C.**
4. __A__ 2 light bulbs in parallel	**D.**
	E. Ⓜ Ⓦ

Draw circuit diagrams as directed below.

5. Draw a circuit diagram showing one resistor and one light bulb in series.	**6.** Draw a circuit diagram showing one resistor and one light bulb in parallel.
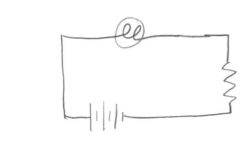	

Use with textbook pages 306–313.

Calculations with series circuits

Use the diagrams to answer the questions below.

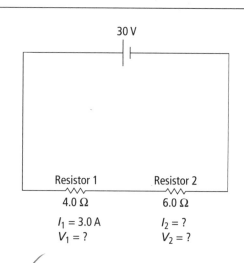

30 V

Resistor 1
4.0 Ω
$I_1 = 3.0$ A
$V_1 = ?$

Resistor 2
6.0 Ω
$I_2 = ?$
$V_2 = ?$

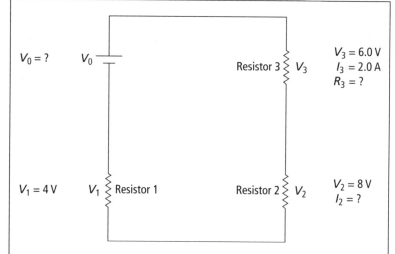

$V_0 = ?$ V_0

$V_3 = 6.0$ V
Resistor 3 V_3 $I_3 = 2.0$ A
$R_3 = ?$

$V_1 = 4$ V V_1 Resistor 1

Resistor 2 V_2 $V_2 = 8$ V
$I_2 = ?$

1. (a) What is the total resistance in the circuit?

10 Ω

(b) What is the amount of current flowing through Resistor 2?

3 Ω

(c) Using Ohm's Law ($V = IR$), determine the voltage drop across Resistor 2.

$V = I \cdot R$

$= 6 \cdot 3$

$= 18$

(d) What is the voltage drop across Resistor 1? ___4 12___

2. (a) What is the total voltage in the circuit?

18 V

(b) What is the amount of current flowing through Resistor 2?

2 8

(c) Ohm's law is $R = \dfrac{V}{I}$. Use Ohm's law to determine the resistance of Resistor 3. ___3.0 R ✓___

Use with textbook pages 306–313.

Series and parallel circuits

Match each Description on the left with the Circuit on the right. Each Circuit may be used more than once.	
Description	**Circuit**
1. __B__ Resistors decrease the total resistance of the circuit.	**A.** series circuit
2. __A__ Resistors increase the total resistance of the circuit.	**B.** parallel circuit
3. __A__ The voltages across each of the loads in the circuit add up to the voltage supplied by the source.	
4. __B__ The voltages across each of the loads in the circuit are equal to each other and to the voltage supplied by the source.	
5. __A__ The current through the whole circuit is the same throughout and is equal to the total current supplied by the source.	
6. __B__ The current through each pathway of the circuit adds up to the total current supplied by the source.	

Circle the letter of the best answer.

Use the following diagram to answer questions 7 and 8.

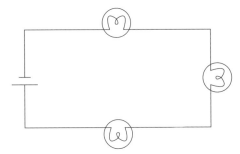

7. The light bulbs are connected in parallel.

A. The statement is correct.

B. The statement is incorrect.

C. The diagram does not show whether the statement is correct or incorrect.

8. The current is the same throughout the entire circuit.

A. The statement is correct.

B. The statement is incorrect.

C. The diagram does not show whether the statement is correct or incorrect.

9. Which of the following statements applies to a series circuit?

I.	There are junction points in the circuit.
II.	There is only one path for electrons to flow.
III.	The total resistance is equal to the sum of the individual resistances.

A. I and II only

B. I and III only

C. II and III only

D. I, II, and III

10. Which of the following applies to a parallel circuit?

A. There is only one path for electrons to flow.

B. Adding a resistor to the circuit increases the total resistance.

C. The sum of the voltages lost on the resistors equals the total voltage supplied by the battery.

D. The total current entering a junction point must equal the sum of the current leaving the junction point.

The Power of Electricity

Textbook pages 320–329

Before You Read

What does the word power mean to you? Write a sentence using this word on the lines below. As you read about the power of electricity in this section, think about how the common meaning of power differs from the scientific meaning.

_____

_____

 Mark the Text

Summarize

As you read this section, highlight the main point in each paragraph. Then write a short paragraph summarizing what you have learned.

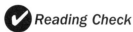 **Reading Check**

1. What is the equation for calculating electrical power?

_____

_____

_____

What is electrical power?

Power is the rate of change in energy. The symbol for power is P. The units for measuring power are joules per second. A **joule** (J) is the unit for measuring energy. One joule per second is also called one **watt** (W).

   Electrical power is the rate of change of electrical energy. In other words, electrical power is the amount of electrical energy that is changed into other forms of energy each second. For example, a 100 W light bulb changes 100 W of electrical energy into light and heat each second.

How is electrical power calculated?

You can calculate electrical power if you know the voltage and current in a circuit:

Power (in watts) = current (in amperes, symbol *I*)
   × voltage (in volts, symbol *V*)
   or $P = IV$

By rearranging the terms in this equation, you can find the current or the voltage of the circuit, too.

$$\text{Current} = \frac{\text{Power}}{\text{Voltage}} \text{ or } I = \frac{P}{V}$$

$$\text{Voltage} = \frac{\text{Power}}{\text{Current}} \text{ or } V = \frac{P}{I}$$ ✓

What is a power rating?

You have likely seen a light bulb with a power in watts marked on it, such as 40 W, 60 W, or 100 W. You may have noticed a similar power in watts on devices such as hair dryers, kettles, or MP3 players. These **power ratings** tell you how many joules of energy the device uses each second of operation. (Recall that 1 W is 1 J/s.)

How is amount of electrical energy calculated?

You can use a power rating to calculate the amount of electrical energy that a device uses. The mathematical equation that defines power is:

$$\textbf{Power (in watts)} = \frac{\text{energy (in joules)}}{\text{time (in seconds)}} \text{ or } P = \frac{E}{t}$$

By rearranging the terms in this equation, you can find the amount of electrical energy that a device uses by multiplying its power rating by the amount of time it was used:

Energy (in joules, J) = Power (in watts, W)

× Time (in seconds, s)

or $E = Pt$ ✔

What is a kilowatt-hour?

A joule is a small amount of energy. You use about one joule of energy to lift a medium-sized apple a distance of one metre. Electrical devices use fairly large amounts of energy, so a larger unit of energy is used to describe them. A **kilowatt-hour** (kW·h) is the same amount of energy as 1000 W used over a period of 1 h.

✔ **Reading Check**

2. What is the equation for calculating energy use of an electrical device?

_____

_____

_____

Power calculations

State the formula that you will be using for each question. Show all your work below. Write down your answer with the correct units.

1. The current in a clothes dryer is 20 A when it is plugged into a 240 V outlet. What is the power rating of this clothes dryer? $P = V \cdot I$ $= 240 \cdot 20$ $= 4800$	**2.** A countertop convection oven is plugged into an outlet that provides a potential difference of 120 V. What is the power rating of the oven if the current is 12 A? $P = V \cdot I$ $= 120 \cdot 12$ $= 1440$
3. A DVD player that is not being used still uses energy at a rate of 15 W. What current is passing through it if the DVD player is plugged into a 120 V electrical outlet? $I = \dfrac{W}{V}$ $= \dfrac{15}{120}$ $= 0.125$	**4.** Determine the amount of current flowing into a 210 W computer plugged into a 120 V outlet. $I = \dfrac{W}{V}$ $= \dfrac{210}{120}$ $= 1.75$
5. A flashlight bulb has 2.4 W of power when the current in the bulb is 0.8 A. What is the voltage drop across the bulb? $V = \dfrac{W}{I}$ $= \dfrac{2.4}{0.8}$ $= 3$	**6.** Calculate the power of the light bulb in the circuit shown below. ③ $I = 2.0$ A 30 V $P = V \cdot I$ $= 30 \cdot 2.0$ $= 60$

Use with textbook pages 320–325.

Energy calculations

State the formula that you will be using for each question. Show all your work below. Write down your answer with the correct units.

1. A microwave oven operates on 1200 W of power and is used for 30 minutes. How much electrical energy is used by the microwave oven? $E = p \times t$ $= (1200w)(1800)$ $= 2,160,000 J$ $P = 1200w$ $t = \dfrac{30 \text{ min}}{= 1800 s}$ $E =$ 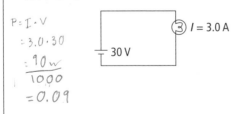	**2.** A refrigerator operates on average for 12 hours a day. If the power rating of the fridge is 700 W, how much electrical energy does the fridge use in one day? $T = 60 \cdot 60$ $= 3600 \cdot 12$ $= 43,200 s$
3. A kitchen light is left on for 6 h. If the amount of electrical energy used is 0.6 kW·h, what is the power rating of the light bulb? $P = \dfrac{E}{T}$ $= \dfrac{0.6 kw}{6 h}$ $= 0.1$ $= 100$	**4.** A hair dryer that has a power rating of 1000 W uses 1.75 kW·h in one week. For how many hours (or minutes) is the hair dryer used daily on average? $P = 1.0$ $E = 1.75$ $T = 0.25 h /day$
5. How much energy did the light bulb in the circuit below use if it was left on for 2 hours? $P = I \cdot V$ $= 3.0 \cdot 30$ $= \dfrac{90 w}{1000}$ $= 0.09$ 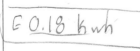 $E\ 0.18\ kwh$ 30 V ③ $I = 3.0$ A 	

Use with textbook pages 320–325.

Paying for electricity

Show all your work below.

1. Assume that the electric utility company charges $0.09 for every kW·h of energy. How much does it cost to:

   (a) operate a dryer that uses 15 A of current at 240 V for 1.5 hours?

   $P = 3600 \text{ W}$
   $= 3.6 \text{ kw}$
   $E = P \cdot t = 3.6 \cdot 1.5 h = 5.4 \text{ kw/h}$ $E = {}^{\$}0.49$

   (b) operate six 100 W light bulbs for an average of 5 hours per day?

   $P = 1000 \text{ w}$
   $\overline{1000}$
   $= 1 \text{ kw}$ $E = P \cdot t = 0.1 \text{ kw} \cdot 5 h = 5 \cdot 6 \cdot 3 = {}^{\$}0.45 \; 0.25$

   (c) operate a refrigerator for a week if it draws 2.0 A of current from a 120 V source that turns on for 15 minutes every hour?

   $P = 240$
   $\overline{1000}$
   $E = P \cdot T = 0.240 \text{ kw} \cdot 6 h \times 7 = 10.08 \cdot 0.09 = 0.9072 / 0.91$

2. If your computer uses 2.5 A at 120 V, how much will it cost to use the computer for 4 hours a day, seven days a week for two weeks? Assume that the cost of electricity is $0.09 for every kW·h of energy.

   _____

   _____

   _____ 1.51 _____

3. A clothes dryer has a power rating of 4000 W. How long did it take to dry a load of laundry if electric power costs $0.09/ kW·h and the cost of using the dryer was $0.54?

   _____

   _____

   _____ 1.5 h _____

Use with textbook pages 320–325.

The power of electricity

Use the following table showing power ratings of some appliances to answer questions 1 to 3.

Appliance	Power (W)
stereo	250
toaster	1100
computer	350
colour TV	200
microwave	900

Match each Description on the left with the correct Appliance on the right. Each Appliance may be used more than once.

Description	Appliance
1. __A__ consumes 1 kW·h of energy if it is left on for 4 h	**A.** stereo
2. __B__ uses the most energy if it operates for 20 min	**B.** toaster
3. __E__ has 7.5 A of current flowing through it when it is plugged into a 120 V outlet	**C.** computer
	D. colour TV
	E. microwave

Circle the letter of the best answer.

4. Which of the following are units for energy?

I.	watts (W)
II.	joules (J)
III.	kilowatt-hours (kW·h)

   A. I and II only

   B. I and III only

   C. II and III only

   D. I, II, and III

5. A calculator uses a 9 V battery and draws 0.2 A of current. What is its power rating?

   A. 0.02 W

   B. 1.8 W

   C. 18 W

   D. 45 W

6. The current flowing in an appliance connected to a 120 V source is 2 A. How much electrical energy does the appliance use in 6 h?

   A. 1.44 kW·h

   B. 40 kW·h

   C. 240 kW·h

   D. 1440 kW·h

7. An electric space heater draws 15 A from a 120 V source. If it is used for 6 hours, how much electrical energy does it use?

I.	10.8 kW·h
II.	648 000 kW·h
III.	38 880 000 J

   A. I and II only

   B. I and III only

   C. II and III only

   D. I, II, and III

8. A self-cleaning oven operates on 5400 W of power when cleaning itself. It takes 2 h to clean. At a cost of $0.09 per kW·h, how much does it cost to clean the oven?

   A. $0.49

   B. $0.97

   C. $10.80

   D. $970.00

Explaining the Early Universe

Textbook pages 346–355

Before You Read

What do you think of when you hear or read the word "universe"? What does the universe include? Record your thoughts on the lines below.

_____

_____

Mark the Text

Identify the Main Point

Skim the section and highlight the main point of each paragraph.

Reading Check

1. How old is the universe, according to the Big Bang theory?

_____

What is the Big Bang theory?

Astronomers are people who study **celestial bodies**, which are objects in space such as stars, the Moon, and planets. Advancements in technology have allowed astronomers to gather evidence about the universe and propose a theory about its origin.

According to the **Big Bang theory**, the universe and everything in it began in an event that took place about 13.7 billion years ago. Before this event, there were no celestial bodies. There was no energy and there was no matter of any kind—not even atoms, protons, or electrons. According to the theory, the Big Bang event gave rise to all the energy and matter in the universe. ✔

What evidence supports the Big Bang theory?

The theory speculates that the universe must have started out very small, hot, and dense and has been expanding and cooling ever since. Evidence for the Big Bang theory includes the following:

◆ Galaxies, which are collections of stars, are moving away from each other. In other words, the universe appears to be expanding.

◆ There is background **radiation**, which is energy transmitted in waves that can be picked up from every part of space. This radiation was first detected in the 1960s by a radio telescope and may be the remains of the radiation that was given off by the original Big Bang event.

◆ Space probes have mapped the background radiation.

Why do scientists think that the universe is expanding?

Visible light is a spectrum of energy ranging from higher-energy, shorter-wavelength, violet-coloured light to lower-energy, longer-wavelength, red-coloured light. A **spectroscope** is an instrument that can separate white light into its wavelengths of colour.

   If a star is moving toward you, its wavelengths become compressed. They are shifted more toward the violet end of the spectrum. If the star is moving away from you, there is a **red shift**, which means its wavelengths get longer. They are stretched out and shifted toward the red end of the spectrum. This red-shifting of wavelengths has been observed with many individual stars, as well as with collections of stars. Astronomers infer that stars and galaxies are moving away from Earth and away from each other. This movement means that the distance between stars and galaxies of the universe is increasing. In other words, the universe is expanding. ✔

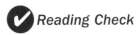

Reading Check

2. What happens to a star's wavelengths as the star moves away from you?

_____

_____

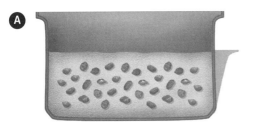

visible light

radio waves | microwaves | infrared radiation | ultraviolet radiation | X rays | gamma rays

red light — └ violet light

1
longer wavelengths   shorter wavelengths

Visible light is part of a larger spectrum of energy.

A model for the expanding universe. The raisins in the uncooked bread dough (A) all move away from each other as the bread bakes (B). In a similar way, galaxies in the universe are moving away from each other as the universe expands.

Use with textbook pages 346–355.

The early days of the universe

Vocabulary	
astronomers	radiation
Big Bang	radio telescope
celestial bodies	red shift
compressed	space probes
galaxies	spectroscope
longer	transmitted

Use the terms in the vocabulary box to fill in the blanks. You can use each term more than once. You will not need to use every term.

1. _____ are people who study objects in space.

2. _____ is a general term for all the objects in space, including the Sun, other stars, planets, and the Moon.

3. _____ is energy that is transmitted in the form of waves.

4. _____ are moving away from each other. In other words, the universe appears to be expanding.

5. An instrument that can separate white light into its wavelengths of colour is the _____.

6. This instrument first detected background radiation in the 1960s: _____.

7. Background radiation has been mapped by _____.

8. The term _____ is used when wavelengths of a star become longer as it moves away from you.

9. If a star is moving toward you, its wavelengths become _____.

10. The theory that suggests that 13.7 billion years ago a tiny volume of space suddenly and rapidly expanded to an immense size is the _____ theory.

Use with textbook pages 348–349.

True or false?

Read the statements given below. If the statement is true, write "T" on the line in front of the statement. If it is false, write "F" and rewrite the statement to make it true.

1. _____ According to the Big Bang theory, when the universe began it was small, dense, and extremely cold.

_____

_____

2. _____ The Big Bang theory has now been proven to be true.

_____

3. _____ According to the Big Bang theory, the universe began 17.3 billion years ago.

_____

_____

4. _____ The universe appears to be compressing because galaxies and stars are moving toward each other.

_____

_____

5. _____ Background radiation is transmitted in waves that were first detected by a spectroscope in the 1960s.

_____

_____

6. _____ If a star is moving toward you, there is a red shift, which means its wavelengths get longer.

_____

_____

7. _____ The distance between stars and galaxies of the universe is decreasing.

_____

Use with textbook pages 346–352.

Modelling an expanding universe

Examine the diagrams below. Then answer the questions.

dough

raisins

Dough for raisin bread, before baking   Baked raisin bread

1. How do the raisins in the dough model an expanding universe?

_____

_____

2. Draw and label your own model of an expanding universe.

3. How does your example model an expanding universe?

_____

_____

Use with textbook pages 346–355.

Explaining the early universe

Match each Term on the left with the best Descriptor on the right. Each Descriptor may only be used once.	
Term	**Descriptor**
1. _____ Big Bang theory **2.** _____ celestial bodies **3.** _____ red shift **4.** _____ radiation **5.** _____ spectroscope **6.** _____ astronomer	**A.** the Sun, other stars, the Moon, and planets **B.** occurs as the object moves away from Earth **C.** occurs as the object moves toward Earth **D.** studies objects in space **E.** the universe formed approximately 13.7 billion years ago **F.** separates light into its basic component colours **G.** energy that is carried in the form of waves

Circle the letter of the best answer.

7. Evidence indicates that galaxies are

  A. stationary

  B. moving away from each other

  C. moving towards each other

  D. always changing direction

8. The Big Bang theory

  A. is now an accepted fact

  B. states that galaxies make a loud sound when they collide

  C. states that the universe began with an event

  D. does not yet have evidence to support it

9. Which of the following statements are correct?

I.	Radio telescopes have detected the background radiation.
II.	Spectroscopes have shifted the background radiation toward the red end of the spectrum.
III.	Space probes have mapped the background radiation.
IV.	Astronomers have transmitted the background radiation.

  A. I and III only

  B. II and IV only

  C. I, II, and III only

  D. I, II, III, and IV

10. If a star is moving toward you,

  A. its wavelengths become compressed

  B. its wavelengths get longer

  C. its wavelengths do not change

  D. its wavelengths cannot be accurately measured

11. If a star is moving away from you,

  A. its wavelengths become compressed

  B. its wavelengths get longer

  C. its wavelengths do not change

  D. its wavelengths cannot be accurately measured

Galaxies

Textbook pages 356–363

Before You Read

How many stars do you think there are in the universe? Record your ideas on the lines below and explain how you chose your answer.

_____

_____

Mark the Text

Summarize

As you read this section, highlight the main point in each paragraph. Then write a short paragraph summarizing what you have learned.

 **Reading Check**

1. What is a galaxy?

_____

_____

_____

What is a galaxy?

A galaxy is a huge group of stars, gas, and dust that is held together by gravity. There might be as many as several billion galaxies in the universe and each galaxy might contain billions of stars. Our own star, the Sun, is part of a galaxy we call the Milky Way galaxy. A **nebula** is a dense cloud-like collection of gas and dust in space. Some nebulae (plural of nebula) are places where stars are born.

What kinds of galaxy shapes are there?

Galaxies are classified as one of three basic shapes: spiral, elliptical, and irregular.

◆ **Spiral galaxies:** If you could look down at a spiral galaxy from above, it would look like a pinwheel. If you could look at it from the side, along its edge, it would look like a plate with a ball in the centre. Spiral galaxies have lots of gas, dust, and young stars. Our own Milky Way galaxy is a spiral galaxy.

Spiral galaxy

◆ **Elliptical galaxies:** An ellipse has the shape of a flattened circle. Elliptical galaxies come in a variety of shapes that range from a perfect sphere to a stretched-out sphere, like a football. Astronomers think that over half of all galaxies in the universe are elliptical. The stars in elliptical galaxies are the oldest stars in the universe, and there is very little gas and dust.

Elliptical galaxy

◆ **Irregular galaxies:** Galaxies that do not have any regular type of shape like a sphere or a pinwheel are called irregular galaxies. Irregular galaxies have lots of gas and dust, which are the building blocks of stars.

Irregular galaxy

How are star clusters different from galaxies?

Star clusters are groups of stars that are found within galaxies. There are two main types of star clusters. Globular clusters are collections of 100 000 to 1 000 000 stars held together by gravity. These groups of stars are arranged in spherical shapes. Open clusters, on the other hand, are collections of up to a few thousand stars. These stars tend to be roughly the same age. ✔

✔ Reading Check

2. What is a star cluster?

_____

_____

_____

Use with textbook pages 356–360.

Inside a galaxy

Vocabulary	
billion	Milky Way
dust	nebula
elliptical	open
galaxy	spiral
gas	star clusters
globular	stars
gravity	thousand
irregular	

Use the terms in the vocabulary box to fill in the blanks. You can use each term more than once. You will not need to use every term.

1. A galaxy is a huge group of _____, _____, and
   _____ that is held together by _____.

2. There might be as many as several _____ galaxies in the
   universe and each galaxy might contain more than a _____
   stars.

3. A(n) _____ is a dense cloud-like collection of gas
   and dust in space.

4. If you could look down at a _____ galaxy from above,
   it would look like a pinwheel.

5. The Sun is part of the _____ galaxy,
   which is a type of _____ galaxy.

6. A(n) _____ galaxy has the shape of a flattened circle.

7. Galaxies that do not have any regular type of shape are called
   _____ galaxies.

8. _____ and _____ are the building
   blocks of stars.

9. Groups of stars within galaxies are called _____.

10. _____ clusters are collections of 100 000 to 1 000 000 stars
    arranged in spherical shapes.

11. _____ clusters are collections of up to a few thousand stars
    that are roughly the same age.

Use with textbook pages 358–359.

All about galaxies

Answer the questions below.

1. What is a galaxy?

_____

_____

2. What are the three basic shapes of galaxies?

_____

_____

3. What type of galaxy is the Milky Way?

_____

4. Which type of galaxy contains the oldest stars in the universe?

_____

5. What is found in an irregular galaxy?

_____

_____

6. What is the percentage of galaxies that are elliptical, approximately?

_____

_____

7. What are the two types of star clusters?

_____

_____

8. How do the two types of star clusters differ?

_____

_____

Use with textbook pages 358–359.

Galaxy shapes

Draw a diagram that represents each of the galaxy shapes. Next to each diagram, briefly describe the characteristics of that type of galaxy.

Spiral galaxy	
Diagram:	Description:

Elliptical galaxy	
Diagram:	Description:

Irregular galaxy	
Diagram:	Description:

Use with textbook pages 356–360.

Galaxies

Match each Term on the left with the best Descriptor on the right. Each Descriptor may only be used once.	
Term	**Descriptor**
1. _____ elliptical galaxy 2. _____ galaxy 3. _____ irregular galaxy 4. _____ nebula 5. _____ spiral galaxy 6. _____ star clusters	**A.** ranges in shape from a perfect sphere to an elongated but flattened ellipse **B.** distinct formations of stars in a galaxy **C.** looks somewhat like a pinwheel **D.** not shaped like a sphere or a pinwheel **E.** a collection of a few thousand stars **F.** a cloud of gas and dust in space **G.** enormous collection of gases, dust, and billions of stars held together by gravity

Circle the letter of the best answer.

7. Earth's Sun is found in what type of galaxy?

   A. elliptical

   B. irregular

   C. spiral

   D. nebula

8. Which type of galaxy holds the oldest stars in the universe?

   A. spiral

   B. elliptical

   C. irregular

   D. star clusters

9. What holds globular clusters of stars together?

   A. gravity

   B. mass

   C. collision

   D. rotation

10. Star clusters vary in the number of stars they contain. What is the approximate range for the number of stars found in an open cluster?

    A. fewer than 10

    B. a few thousand

    C. 1000 to 1 000 000

    D. 100 000 to 100 000 000

11. Astronomers think that over half of all galaxies in the universe are

    A. elliptical

    B. irregular

    C. spiral

    D. spherical

12. Which is true of the Milky Way galaxy?

I.	has the shape of a flattened circle
II.	from above it looks like a pin-wheel
III.	has lots of young stars
IV.	from the side it looks like a plate with a ball in the centre

    A. I, II, and III only

    B. I, III, and IV only

    C. II, III, and IV only

    D. I, II, III, and IV

Stars

Textbook pages 368–381

Before You Read

What is a star made from? How long does a star last? Write your ideas on the lines below.

_____

_____

 Mark the Text

Reinforce Your Understanding

As you read this section, highlight the main point of each paragraph. Use a different colour to highlight an example that helps explain the main point, or write your own example.

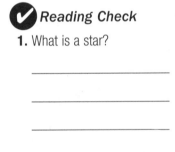 **Reading Check**

1. What is a star?

_____

_____

_____

_____

What is a star?

A **star** is a massive, gaseous, spherical object in space that gives off light and other forms of energy due to nuclear reactions that take place at its core. These nuclear reactions transform elements of one kind into elements of another kind. For instance, during most of the life of a star, atoms of hydrogen gas fuse and become atoms of helium gas. This nuclear change, called nuclear **fusion**, releases tremendous amounts of energy. ✓

What does the colour of a star reveal?

If a piece of metal is heated, its colour changes. The colour is red at first. Then, as the metal gets hotter, the colour becomes orange, then yellow, and then blue-white. Stars differ in colour, and we can infer their surface temperature based on their colour. Yellow stars, such as our Sun, are fairly hot, with a surface temperature of about 6000°C. Red stars are fairly cool, about 3000°C. Whitish-blue stars are extremely hot, ranging from 20 000°C to 40 000°C.

The colour of a star also reveals clues about what the star is made of and how it is moving. When the wavelength of the light from an object changes due to its motion, the change is called the **Doppler effect**.

How long do stars last?

The "life" of a star depends on its mass. Low mass stars (red dwarf stars) use up their hydrogen slowly and can last as long as 100 billion years. As they use up their hydrogen, they lose mass and end their lives as small, dim white dwarf stars.

Intermediate mass stars like our Sun use up their hydrogen more quickly—over about 10 billion years. When the hydrogen is used up, the core of the star contracts, the temperature rises, and the outer layers of the star expand. These cooler outer layers have a red colour, so stars at this stage of their lives are called red giants. As they continue to age, they get smaller, cooler, and dimmer, becoming a white dwarf and, eventually, an even cooler, darker black dwarf star.

High mass stars use up their hydrogen relatively quickly, and may only last millions of years. When nearing the end of its life, the core of a high mass star collapses in a dramatic, powerful explosion called a **supernova**. For very high mass stars, the remaining core contracts further, resulting in a rapidly rotating, unimaginably dense neutron star. ✔

What is a black hole?

Astronomers believe that the core of an extremely massive star can contract greatly into a super-compact, super-dense object called a **black hole**. The force of gravity in a black hole is so great that not even light can escape it.

✔ *Reading Check*

2. When does a supernova occur?

_____

_____

_____

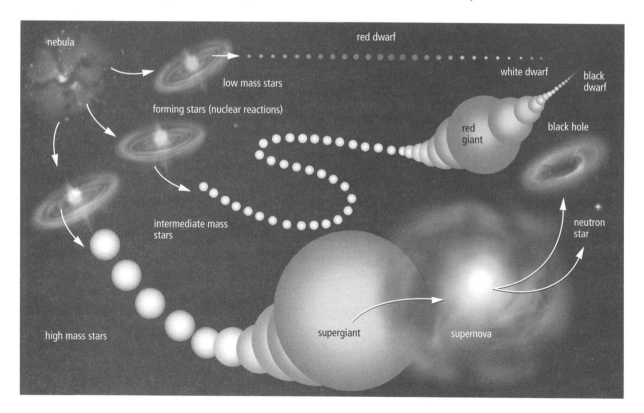

nebula
red dwarf
low mass stars
forming stars (nuclear reactions)
white dwarf
black dwarf
red giant
black hole
intermediate mass stars
neutron star
high mass stars
supergiant
supernova

Use with textbook pages 368–377.

Describing stars

Vocabulary	
black dwarf	red
black hole	red dwarf
Doppler	red giants
fusion	supernova
helium	white dwarf
hydrogen	whitish-blue
mass	yellow
neutron	

Use the terms in the vocabulary box to fill in the blanks. Each term can be used more than once. You will not need to use every term.

1. During most of the life of a star, atoms of _____ gas fuse and become atoms of _____ gas. This nuclear change, called nuclear _____, releases tremendous amounts of energy.

2. Stars that are _____ in colour, such as our Sun, are fairly hot, with a surface temperature of about 6000°C.

3. Stars that are _____ in colour are fairly cool, about 3000°C.

4. Stars that are _____ in colour are extremely hot, ranging from 20 000°C to 40 000°C.

5. When the wavelength of a star's light changes due to its motion, the change is called the _____ effect.

6. The "life" of a star depends on its _____.

7. Low mass stars, called _____ stars, use up their hydrogen slowly.

8. As they continue to age, intermediate mass stars get smaller, cooler, and dimmer, becoming a _____ and, eventually, an even cooler, darker _____ star.

9. When nearing the end of its life, the core of a high mass star collapses in a dramatic, powerful explosion called a _____. For very high mass stars, the remaining core contracts further, resulting in a rapidly rotating, unimaginably dense _____ star.

10. The core of an extremely massive star can contract greatly into a super-compact, super-dense object called a _____.

Use textbook pages 370–372.

The evolution of stars

The diagrams below illustrate the changes two types of stars go through as they age. Describe the life cycle of each type of star and answer the question that follows.

Different life paths for stars
1. Low mass stars
Description
_____
_____
2. Intermediate mass stars
Description
_____
_____

3. How does a high mass star end its life? _____

_____

Use with textbook pages 368–377.

True or false?

Read the statements given below. If the statement is true, write "T" on the line in front of the statement. If it is false, write "F" and then rewrite the statement so it is true.

1. _____ A star gives off light due to interstellar reactions that take place at its core.

   _____

   _____

2. _____ During most of the life of a star, atoms of helium gas fuse and become atoms of hydrogen gas.

   _____

   _____

3. _____ Yellow stars, such as our Sun, are the hottest types of stars.

   _____

4. _____ The colour of a star reveals information about what the star is made of, its temperature, and how it is moving.

   _____

   _____

5. _____ Intermediate mass stars expand into red giants and then become part of a supernova.

   _____

   _____

6. _____ A high mass star may last only millions of years.

   _____

7. _____ The force of gravity is so strong in black holes that not even light can escape from them.

   _____

   _____

Use with textbook pages 368–377.

Stars

Match each Term on the left with the best Descriptor on the right. Each Descriptor may be used only once.	
Term	**Descriptor**
1. _____ black hole **2.** _____ fusion **3.** _____ star **4.** _____ supernova	**A.** a dramatic, massive explosion that occurs when a large, high mass star collapses in on itself **B.** super-compact, super-dense celestial object **C.** a spherical celestial body of hot gases that gives off light due to nuclear reactions **D.** the process in which atoms fuse together to form other atoms **E.** a rapidly rotating, unimaginably dense celestial body

Circle the letter of the best answer.

5. Hydrogen atoms combine to form helium in a process called

   A. nuclear fusion

   B. nuclear fission

   C. supernova

   D. nuclear burnout

6. Which type of star has an average life of 10 billion years?

   A. low mass star

   B. intermediate mass star

   C. high mass star

   D. all stars

7. A low mass star will eventually become a

   A. red giant

   B. nebula

   C. supernova

   D. white dwarf

8. When comparing the sizes of stars, our Sun is

   A. the largest star discovered to date

   B. one of the larger stars discovered to date

   C. medium size as compared to other stars

   D. one of the smallest stars discovered to date

9. What is the temperature range for whitish-blue stars?

   A. 1000°C to 3000°C

   B. 2000°C to 4000°C

   C. 5000°C to 6000°C

   D. 20 000°C to 40 000°C

10. What information can astronomers gain from the colour of a star?

    A. the star's temperature and composition

    B. the nebula the star came from

    C. the stage of development the star is in

    D. the direction the star might go in next

11. Which of the following is not true of high mass stars?

    A. They use up hydrogen relatively slowly.

    B. They last only millions of years.

    C. They collapse in a supernova.

    D. Their core may contract further into a neutron star.

The Sun and Its Planetary System

Textbook pages 382–395

Before You Read

How many types of celestial bodies can you name? Write down as many as you know on the lines below.

_____

_____

 **Mark the Text**

Identify Details

As you skim the section, use one colour to highlight the text or labels that talk about the parts of the Sun. Use another colour to highlight text that talks about the other parts of the solar system.

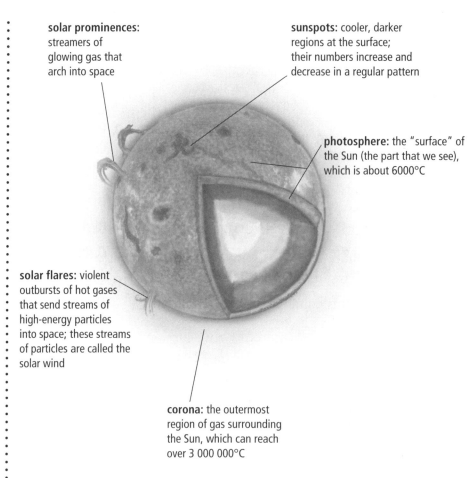

solar prominences: streamers of glowing gas that arch into space

sunspots: cooler, darker regions at the surface; their numbers increase and decrease in a regular pattern

photosphere: the "surface" of the Sun (the part that we see), which is about 6000°C

solar flares: violent outbursts of hot gases that send streams of high-energy particles into space; these streams of particles are called the solar wind

corona: the outermost region of gas surrounding the Sun, which can reach over 3 000 000°C

The Sun

What is the Sun like?

The Sun is a huge sphere of mostly hydrogen gas. The nuclear reactions that take place at its core generate heat, light, and other forms of energy that radiate outward in all directions. Over 110 Earths could fit across the Sun's diameter. Some parts of the Sun are shown in the diagram above.

How did the planets of the solar system form?

A **solar system** is a group of planets circling a star. A **planet** is a spherical object made mainly of rock or gases, which orbits a star and is large enough that its own gravity holds it in a spherical shape. Planets spin on an imaginary line called an **axis**—a motion called **rotation**. Planets also travel around the Sun—a motion called **revolution**. ✔

A widely accepted hypothesis states that the planets began to form from the gases and other matter left over after the Sun formed. The rocky bodies closest to the new Sun were blasted with its radiation. Because they did not have enough gravity to hold much of their hot atmospheres, they became the rocky, inner planets: Mercury, Venus, Earth, and Mars. Farther out, away from the Sun's intense heat, the outer planets kept their gases. They became the gas giants, the remaining planets of the solar system: Jupiter, Saturn, Uranus, and Neptune.

All planets except for Mercury and Venus have at least one moon. A **moon** is an object that orbits a planet.

What other objects make up the solar system?

Throughout much of the early history of the solar system, stray rocky material and dust pounded the planets and their moons. Craters are evidence of these interactions. Some of this rocky material remains in the form of **asteroids**—small objects that orbit the Sun, mainly found between Mars and Jupiter. Rocky material left over from the formation of the solar system is also found at its outer limits in a region called the Oort cloud. From this region come **comets**—objects made of rock and ice that orbit the Sun. ✔

✔ **Reading Check**

1. What is the difference between rotation and revolution?

_____

_____

_____

_____

_____

✔ **Reading Check**

2. Name two types of solar-system objects that are not planets, stars, or moons.

_____

_____

_____

Use with textbook pages 382–389.

Getting to know the solar system

Vocabulary	
asteroids	Neptune
axis	nuclear reactions
comets	revolution
Earth	rotation
helium	Saturn
hydrogen	solar flares
Jupiter	solar prominences
Mars	solar wind
Mercury	Uranus
moon	Venus

Use the terms in the vocabulary box to fill in the blanks. You can use terms more than once. You will not need to use every term.

1. The Sun is a huge sphere of mostly _____ gas.

2. The _____ that take place at the Sun's core generate heat, light, and other forms of energy that radiate outward in all directions.

3. The streamers of glowing gas that arch into space from the Sun are called _____ .

4. The violent outbursts of hot gases from the Sun that send streams of high-energy particles into space are called _____ .
   These streams of particles are called the _____ .

5. Planets spin on an imaginary line called a(n) _____ in a motion called _____ .

6. Planets travel around the Sun in a motion called _____ .

7. The rocky, inner planets include _____, _____, _____, and _____ .

8. The planets that are gas giants include _____ , _____ , _____ , and _____ .

9. All planets except for Mercury and Venus have at least one _____ .

10. Small objects that orbit the Sun and are mainly found between Mars and Jupiter are called _____ .

11. Objects made of rock and ice that orbit the Sun and come from the Oort cloud are called _____ .

Use with textbook pages 383–384.

Features of the Sun

Match each feature of the Sun on the left with its description on the right. Then label the parts of the diagram. Each description may be used only once.

Feature of the Sun	Description
1. _____ corona **2.** _____ photosphere **3.** _____ solar flares **4.** _____ solar prominences **5.** _____ sunspots	**A.** streamers of glowing gas that arch into space **B.** cooler, darker regions at the surface; their numbers increase and decrease in a regular pattern **C.** violent outbursts of hot gases that send streams of high-energy particles into space; these streams of particles are called the solar wind **D.** the "surface" of the Sun, which is about 6000°C **E.** the outermost region of gas surrounding the Sun, which can reach over 3 000 000°C

6. Label this diagram of the Sun.

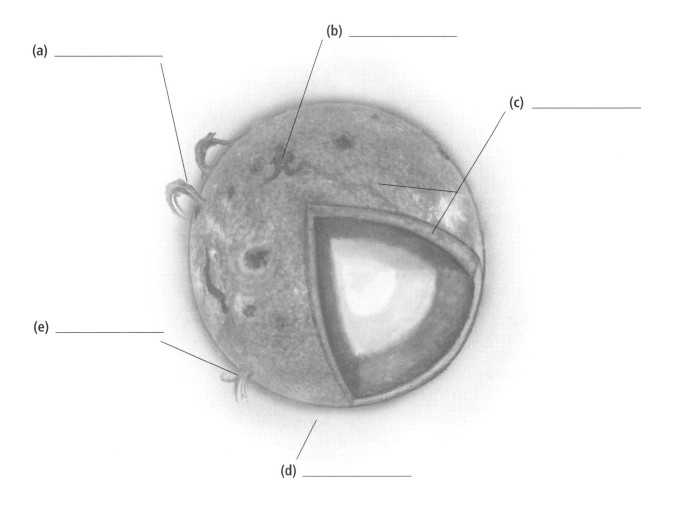

(a) _____

(b) _____

(c) _____

(e) _____

(d) _____

Use with textbook pages 382–389.

Our solar system

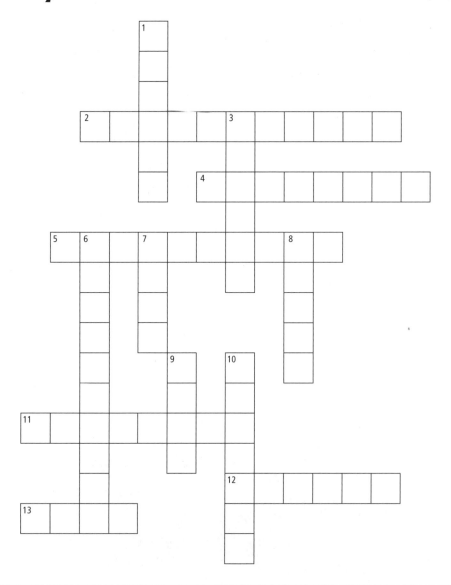

Across	Down
2. the part of the Sun that we see	1. the outermost part of the Sun's atmosphere
4. small rocky body; many of these orbit the Sun between Mars and Jupiter	3. a collection of planets orbiting a star is called a solar ___
5. a streamer of glowing gas that arches into space is called a solar ___	6. the motion of Earth as it orbits the Sun
11. the motion of Earth as it spins on its axis	7. a celestial body that orbits a planet
12. a celestial body that orbits a star	8. a small body of rocky material and ice from the Oort Cloud
13. streams of high-energy particles are called the solar ___	9. an imaginary line through a planet
	10. cooler, darker region on sun's surface

Use with textbook pages 382–389.

The Sun and its planetary system

Match each Term on the left with the best Descriptor on the right. Each Descriptor may be used only once.	
Term	**Descriptor**
1. _____ asteroid 2. _____ axis 3. _____ comet 4. _____ moon 5. _____ planet 6. _____ revolution 7. _____ rotation 8. _____ solar system	**A.** an imaginary line through Earth **B.** a celestial body that orbits a star and is large enough that its own gravity holds it in a spherical shape **C.** a small body made up of rock and ice **D.** a small rocky body that orbits the Sun between Mars and Jupiter **E.** the motion of Earth as it orbits the Sun **F.** a celestial body that orbits a planet **G.** a group of planets circling a star **H.** a stream of high-energy particles **I.** the motion of Earth as it spins on its axis

Circle the letter of the best answer.

9. The Sun is mainly made up of

   A. hydrogen gas

   B. oxygen gas

   C. a combination of hydrogen and oxygen gases

   D. a combination of hydrogen and methane gases

10. What is a solar prominence?

    A. dark patch on the surface of the Sun

    B. large arch of super-hot gas that extends out from the Sun's surface

    C. the outermost part of the Sun's atmosphere

    D. the thin layer on the outside of the Sun

11. When high-energy particles rush past Earth, what is created?

    A. sunspots

    B. comets

    C. convection currents

    D. solar wind

12. Where are most asteroids found in the solar system?

    A. beyond Jupiter

    B. beyond Neptune

    C. between Earth and Mars

    D. between Mars and Jupiter

13. Where is the Oort cloud found?

    A. the surface of the Sun

    B. between Earth and Mars

    C. the outer limits of the solar system

    D. beyond the solar system

14. Which of the following correctly identifies the planets?

	Gas giants	Rocky planets
I.	Mercury, Venus	Earth, Jupiter
II.	Jupiter, Saturn	Mercury, Venus
III.	Saturn, Venus	Mars, Jupiter
IV.	Venus, Saturn	Earth, Mars

    A. I

    B. II

    C. III

    D. IV

Measuring Distances in Space

Textbook pages 396–405

Before You Read

Looking at stars is like looking into the past. What might be the reason why? Record your thoughts on the lines below.

_____

_____

Mark the Text

In Your Own Words

Highlight the main idea in each paragraph. Stop after each paragraph and put what you just read into your own words.

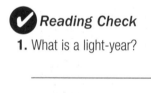
Reading Check

1. What is a light-year?

_____

_____

_____

How big is the universe?

Distances between most objects in space are so great that it is hard to imagine them. The unit that is commonly used to describe distances in space is the light-year. To understand this unit, think first about light. Scientists believe that light moves faster than anything else in the universe. Light moves at a speed of nearly 300 000 km/s. How fast is that? In the time it takes to snap your fingers, light can travel around the entire Earth more than seven times.

Travelling at 300 000 km/s, light from the Sun takes about 8 min to reach Earth. Light from the Sun takes about 5 h to reach Neptune, the most distant planet in our solar system. But to reach the star that is nearest to us, called Proxima Centauri, light must travel about 4.2 *years*. A **light-year** represents the distance that light travels in one year. So the distance to Proxima Centauri is 4.2 light-years. Most stars in the universe are hundreds, thousands, and even *millions* of light-years away from us. Can you imagine that? Can anyone? The universe is huge! ✔

How can distances in space be measured?

Long ago, people invented a technique for calculating distances on the ground indirectly: triangulation. **Triangulation** involves creating an imaginary triangle between an observer and the object. To use triangulation, you need to know the length of one side of the triangle, called the baseline. You also need to know the size of the two angles created when imaginary lines are drawn from each end of the baseline to the same point on the distant object.

For thousands of years people measured the distances to stars using triangulation and an effect called parallax. **Parallax**

is the apparent change in position of a nearby object when it is viewed from two different points. You can see this effect by pointing at a distant object with your finger. Then, keeping your finger in view, blink first one eye and then the other. Your fingertip appears to move compared with the background because you are viewing your finger from two different points. In this case, the baseline is the distance between your eyes. ✔

To measure distances from Earth to stars, the longest possible baseline is the diameter of Earth's orbit. Sightings have to be taken six months apart. This is the time it takes Earth to move from one end of its orbital baseline to the other. If a star is close enough (up to 1000 light-years), it will appear to move in relation to the more distant stars. Then its distance can be determined using triangulation.

✔ *Reading Check*

2. What is the longest possible baseline for measuring distances from Earth to stars?

_____

_____

_____

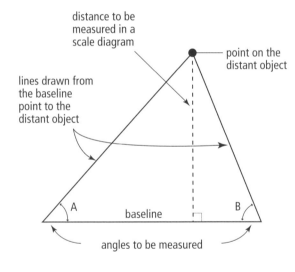

distance to be measured in a scale diagram

point on the distant object

lines drawn from the baseline point to the distant object

A

baseline

B

angles to be measured

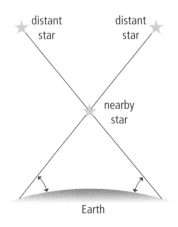

distant star

distant star

nearby star

Earth

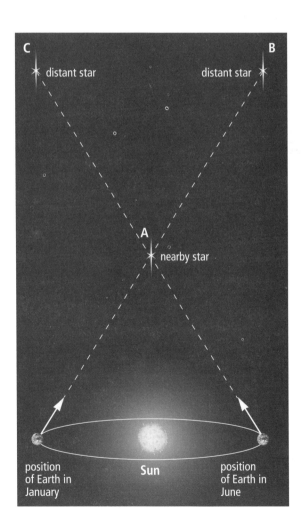

C   distant star

B   distant star

A   nearby star

position of Earth in January

Sun

position of Earth in June

Use with textbook pages 396–401.

Describing distances in space

Vocabulary	
300 000 km/s	months
300 000 m/s	parallax
baseline	seconds
distance	shift
hours	triangle
light	triangulation
light-year	width
minutes	years

Use the terms in the vocabulary box to fill in the blanks. Each term can be used more than once. You will not need to use every term.

1. The unit that is commonly used to describe distances in space is the

   _____.

2. Light moves at a speed of nearly _____.

3. Light from the Sun takes about 4.2 _____ to reach the nearest star, about 5 _____ to reach the farthest planet in the solar system, and about 8 _____ to reach Earth.

4. _____ involves creating an imaginary triangle between an observer and the object.

5. An ancient technique for measuring the distances to stars involves the effect of

   _____.

6. _____ is the apparent change in position of a nearby object when it is viewed from two different points.

7. To measure distances from Earth to stars, the longest possible _____ is the diameter of Earth's orbit.

8. The time it takes Earth to move from one end of its orbital baseline to the other is 6 _____.

Use with textbook page 401.

Parallax

Mercury   Venus   Earth   Mars   Jupiter   Saturn   Uranus   Neptune

**You can demonstrate the principles of parallax. Set your workbook in an upright
position, open to this page. Use the diagram above as your background for this
activity.**

1. Hold a pencil in front of your face at about one arm's length. Blink your eyes, one at
   a time, while looking at the pencil. How does the image of the pencil change when
   you do this?

   _____

2. Hold a pencil in front of your face at about one half of an arm's length. Blink your
   eyes, one at a time, while looking at the pencil. How does the image of the pencil
   change when you do this?

   _____

3. Hold a pencil in front of your face at about 5 cm from your eyes. Blink your eyes, one
   at a time, while looking at the pencil. How does the image of the pencil change when
   you do this?

   _____

4. As you moved the pencil closer, what observations were you able to make about the
   size of the shift of the pencil image?

   _____

5. As the distance from your eyes to the pencil increases, what do you think would
   happen to the size of the shift of the pencil image?

   _____

6. What vocabulary term could be used to describe this shifting?

   _____

Use with textbook pages 396–397.

How big is space?

Vocabulary	
Mount Robson	human
distance from Earth to Proxima Centauri	the Moon
Earth	observable universe
~~electron~~	single-cell organism
galaxy	solar system
gray whale	the Sun

Which is bigger, Earth or an asteroid? Think about the relative size of each of the things in the vocabulary box. Figure out their order from smallest to largest. Then list them from the smallest objects (1) to the largest (12). The smallest one has been done for you.

1. _____ electron _____

2. _____

3. _____

4. _____

5. _____

6. _____

7. _____

8. _____

9. _____

10. _____

11. _____

12. _____

Use with textbook pages 396–401.

Measuring distances in space

Match each Term on the left with the best Descriptor on the right. Each Descriptor may be used only once.	
Term	**Descriptor**
1. _____ light-year 2. _____ parallax 3. _____ triangulation	**A.** the apparent shift of an object against a stationary background by the change in position of the observer **B.** a technique for determining the distance to a visible object by creating an imaginary triangle between the observer and the object and then calculating the distance **C.** a measurement equal to the average distance from the Sun and Earth **D.** the distance that light travels in a year

Circle the letter of the best answer.

4. What does a light-year measure?

   A. time

   B. distance

   C. velocity

   D. diameter

5. What is the speed that light travels at?

   A. 300 km/s

   B. 3000 km/s

   C. 30 000 km/s

   D. 300 000 km/s

6. Ancient astronomers calculated distances using

   A. triangulation and geometry

   B. triangulation and parallax

   C. geometry and probability

   D. parallax and estimation

7. When observing a stationary object against a background, if you blink your eyes, one at a time, the object will appear to

   A. stay in one place

   B. disappear

   C. shift position

   D. rotate

8. The principle demonstrated in question 7 is known as

   A. triangulation

   B. geometry

   C. Newton's law

   D. parallax

9. Approximately how long does it take light from the Sun to reach Earth?

   A. 8 s

   B. 8 min

   C. 8 h

   D. 8 light-years

10. What is the longest possible baseline for measuring distances from Earth to stars?

   A. the distance from Earth to the Sun

   B. the distance from Earth to the Moon

   C. the diameter of Earth

   D. the diameter of Earth's orbit

Earth, Moon, and Sun Interactions

Textbook pages 410–425

Before You Read

For thousands of years, people believed that the Sun travelled around Earth. What observation did they base this on? Record your ideas on the lines below.

_____

_____

State the Main Ideas

As you read this section, stop after each paragraph and put what you have just read into your own words.

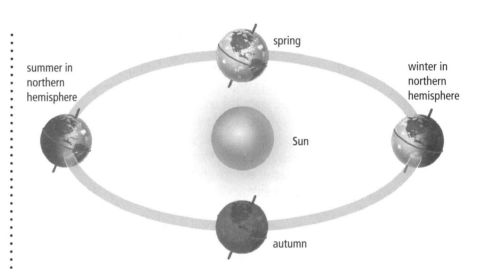

Reading Check

1. How does the tilt of Earth's axis affect the way sunlight falls on Earth's surface?

_____

_____

_____

What causes the seasons?

Earth's axis is tilted on an angle of 23.5°. This **axis tilt** causes light from the Sun to strike Earth at different angles during its orbit around the Sun. As Earth orbits the Sun, Earth's axis always points in the same direction. However, the amount of sunlight that falls on Earth's surface at different points in its journey is different. This difference is what causes the seasons. ✔

How did the Moon form?

Scientists think that long ago, as Earth and other inner planets were forming, a huge, planet-sized object slammed into Earth. The intense impact ejected large and small pieces of the young planet. These pieces went into orbit around Earth and, over time, built up into the object that we know today as the Moon.

What is an eclipse?

An eclipse is the total or partial blocking of sunlight that occurs when one object in space passes in front of another. There are two kinds: solar eclipses and lunar eclipses. Both types involve the interaction of the Sun, Earth, and Moon. ✓

In a **solar eclipse**, the Moon passes between the Sun and Earth, briefly blocking our view of the Sun. People who observe where the full shadow of the Moon falls on Earth's surface see a total solar eclipse. People who observe where only part of the Moon's shadow falls see a partial solar eclipse.

In a **lunar eclipse**, Earth passes between the Sun and the Moon, briefly plunging the Moon into darkness as Earth's shadow moves across it. When the Moon lies fully in Earth's shadow, people see a total lunar eclipse.

What are constellations?

As viewed from Earth, stars seem to make unchanging patterns in the night sky. These patterns look like familiar objects, which people long ago grouped and named. These groupings of stars into familiar patterns and shapes are called **constellations**. Stars in the night sky all look as if they are close to one another and equal distances from Earth. In reality, all stars are separated from one another and from us by hundreds, thousands, or millions of light-years.

Because stars and other sky objects look as if they move around Earth, Greek astronomer **Ptolemy** and many other people several thousand years ago thought that Earth was at the centre of the universe. In the early 1500s, a Polish astronomer named **Copernicus** proposed a model of the heavens in which planets, including a rotating Earth, revolved around the Sun. Italian astronomer **Galileo** confirmed Copernicus' model. In the early 1600s, a German mathematician named **Kepler** predicted that the planets revolved around the Sun in elliptical orbits, not circles as was thought. An ellipse is the shape of a flattened circle.

✔ **Reading Check**

2. What is an eclipse?

_____

_____

_____

Use with textbook pages 410–420.

How do Earth, the Sun, and the Moon interact?

Vocabulary	
axis	partial
constellations	Ptolemy
Copernicus	seasons
eclipse	solar
Galileo	total
Kepler	years
lunar	

Use the terms in the vocabulary box to fill in the blanks. Each term may be used more than once. You will not need to use every term.

1. Earth's _____ is tilted on an angle of 23.5°, which causes light from the Sun to strike Earth at different angles during its orbit around the Sun.

2. A(n) _____ is the total or partial blocking of sunlight that occurs when one object in space passes in front of another.

3. In a _____ eclipse, the Moon passes between the Sun and Earth, briefly blocking our view of the Sun.

4. People who observe where the full shadow of the Moon falls on Earth's surface see a _____ solar _____. People who observe where only part of the Moon's shadow falls see a _____ solar _____.

5. In a _____ eclipse, Earth passes between the Sun and the Moon, briefly plunging the Moon into darkness as Earth's shadow moves across it.

6. When the Moon lies fully in Earth's shadow, people see a _____ lunar _____.

7. Groupings of stars that look like familiar patterns are called _____.

8. Greek astronomer _____ thought that Earth was at the centre of the universe.

9. In the early 1500s, a Polish astronomer named _____ proposed a model of the heavens in which planets, including Earth, revolved around the Sun. Italian astronomer _____ confirmed his model.

10. In the early 1600s, a German mathematician named _____ predicted that the planets revolved around the Sun in elliptical orbits.

Use with textbook pages 413–418.

Eclipses

Show what you know about eclipses. Draw diagrams as directed below.

1. Draw a diagram that shows what happens during a solar eclipse. Be sure to label the Sun, Moon, and Earth.

2. Draw a diagram that shows what happens during a lunar eclipse. Be sure to label the Sun, Moon, and Earth.

Use with textbook pages 410–420.

Seasons

Label the diagram, and then answer the question.

1. Label the diagram below according to the seasons for the northern hemisphere.

   - spring
   - summer
   - autumn
   - winter

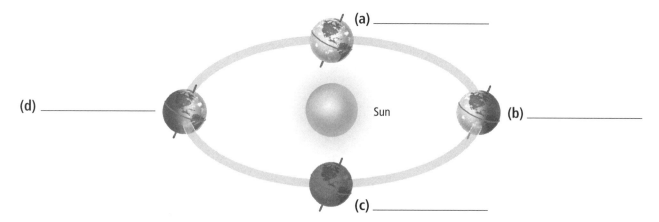

2. Why do we have different seasons? Write a paragraph to explain. Be sure to mention axis tilt and revolution in your answer.

_____

_____

_____

_____

_____

_____

_____

Use with textbook pages 410–420.

Earth, Moon, and Sun interactions

Match each Term on the left with the best Descriptor on the right. Each Descriptor may be used only once.

Term	Descriptor
1. _____ axis tilt **2.** _____ constellations **3.** _____ Copernicus **4.** _____ Galileo **5.** _____ Kepler **6.** _____ lunar eclipse **7.** _____ Ptolemy **8.** _____ solar eclipse	**A.** distinctive patterns formed by groups of stars **B.** occurs when the Moon passes between the Sun and Earth **C.** occurs when the Sun passes between the Moon and Earth **D.** occurs when Earth passes between the Moon and the Sun **E.** Earth's is 23.5° **F.** proposed that the Sun was the centre of the solar system **G.** Greek astronomer who supported that Earth was the centre of the solar system **H.** confirmed Copernicus's model of a solar system **I.** determined that the planets orbit the Sun in elliptical paths

Circle the letter of the best answer.

9. A total solar eclipse occurs when the

   A. full shadow of the Moon falls on Earth

   B. full shadow of the Sun falls on Earth

   C. full shadow of Earth falls on the Moon

   D. full shadow of the Moon falls on the Sun

10. How do scientists think the Moon might have formed?

I.	from pieces of Earth knocked off by a large object
II.	from pieces of Earth in Earth's orbit
III.	from an explosion beneath Earth's surface
IV.	from pieces of other planets passing through space

A. I and II only

B. II and III only

C. III only

D. IV only

11. What causes the seasons?

I.	Earth's axis tilt changes and this causes light from the Sun to strike Earth at different angles during its orbit around the Sun.
II.	Earth's axis tilt changes and this causes light from the Sun to strike Earth at different times during its orbit around the Sun.
III.	Earth's axis tilt causes light from the Sun to strike Earth at different angles during its orbit around the Sun.
IV.	Earth's axis tilt causes light from the Sun to strike Earth at different times during its orbit around the Sun.

A. I

B. II

C. III

D. IV

Aboriginal Knowledge of the Solar System

Textbook pages 426–431

Before You Read

Like all aspects of Aboriginal life, Aboriginal views of the solar system involve respect for all living and non-living things. What does respect for living and non-living things mean? Write your thoughts on the lines below.

_____

_____

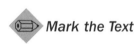

Mark the Text

Summarize

As you read this section, highlight the main point in each paragraph. Then write a short paragraph summarizing what you have learned.

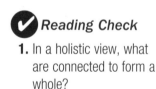

Reading Check

1. In a holistic view, what are connected to form a whole?

_____

_____

_____

What is a holistic view?

Aboriginal peoples, like Western scientists, have long observed the Moon, Sun, planets, and other objects in the sky. They have also theorized about Earth's relationship with all of these sky objects.

Among many Aboriginal peoples, existence is thought to be made up of many interconnected areas, or realms. Common realms include the undersea or sea world, the land world, the spirit world, and the sky world. In a universe where everything is connected, Aboriginal peoples know that each of these realms is also a source of knowledge about all of the other realms. A **holistic** view is one that sees all aspects of the physical and spiritual universe as connected to form a whole.

Western science—the type of science that is learned and practised by most people today—is based mainly on the physical realm. Western science involves the study of events that can be physically observed, measured, documented, and tested. Aboriginal knowledge can also be based on the physical realm. However, Aboriginal knowledge also often uses understanding gained from other realms. When everything is connected, the spiritual realm is as much a source of knowledge as the physical realm. ✔

How do Aboriginal peoples use their knowledge of the sky?

Aboriginal peoples have long used their knowledge of the Moon in their daily lives. The success of Aboriginal peoples who fish on the coast, for example, depends on their knowledge of the phases of the Moon and the Moon's influence on various fish species, the weather, and ocean tides. Mariners navigating coastal waters and harvesters of shellfish, kelp, and other intertidal resources must all be aware of the link between the Moon's phases and low and high tides.

Aboriginal peoples developed a way to track and forecast time based on the lunar month. A **lunar month** is the length of time from one new moon (or one full moon) to the next. The time for this cycle of change is about 29.5 days. The Coast Salish, for example, traditionally use a 13-moon system in which each moon of the year is named and linked with certain cultural activities. The Nuu-chah-nulth also use a 13-month lunar cycle that includes the four seasons. ✓

In many parts of the province, Aboriginal peoples relied on the predictable positions of planets and stars in the night sky for information. With this knowledge, traditional hunters could determine their location on the land. People who fished and mariners could determine their location on the ocean. Many Aboriginal peoples continue to use these methods of tracking and navigating today.

✔ *Reading Check*

2. What is a lunar month?

_____

_____

_____

How does Aboriginal knowledge affect Western science?

Over the past decades, some aspects of Aboriginal knowledge and understanding of the universe have been incorporated into Western science. Aboriginal knowledge of the link between the phases of the Moon and tides, currents, and erosion along parts of the British Columbia coast is now part of the overall body of knowledge about our coastline. Aboriginal observations of constellations are now part of the overall body of knowledge called, in Western science, astronomy.

Use with textbook pages 426–429.

Looking at the solar system

Vocabulary	
12	Moon
13	physical
constellations	realms
holistic	solar month
interconnected universe	spiritual
lunar month	Western

Use the terms in the vocabulary box to fill in the blanks. You can use terms more than once. You will not need to use every term.

1. A _____ approach means that all aspects of the physical and spiritual universe are connected to form a whole.

2. Among many Aboriginal peoples, existence is thought to be made up of a number of interconnected areas, or _____.

3. In the _____, Aboriginal peoples know that these realms cannot be separated.

4. _____ science is based on the physical realm, which involves the study of phenomena that can be physically observed, measured, documented, and tested.

5. When everything is interconnected, the _____ realm is as much a source of knowledge and truth as the _____ realm.

6. Aboriginal peoples who fish on the coast, for example, depend on their knowledge of the influence of the _____ on various fish species, the weather, and ocean tides.

7. Aboriginal peoples developed a means of tracking and forecasting time based on the _____.

8. Traditionally, the lunar year has _____ lunar months.

9. Aboriginal observations of _____ are now part of the overall body of knowledge called astronomy.

Use with textbook pages 426–429.

Comparing Aboriginal knowledge and Western science approaches

Information gained through Aboriginal knowledge and Western science is often very similar. However, many aspects from the two approaches are different.

1. Use a Venn diagram to help you compare the two approaches. On the left side of the Venn diagram, write points that apply to traditional Aboriginal approaches to the solar system. On the right side, write points that apply to Western science approaches to the solar system. In the middle, write approaches that are common to both.

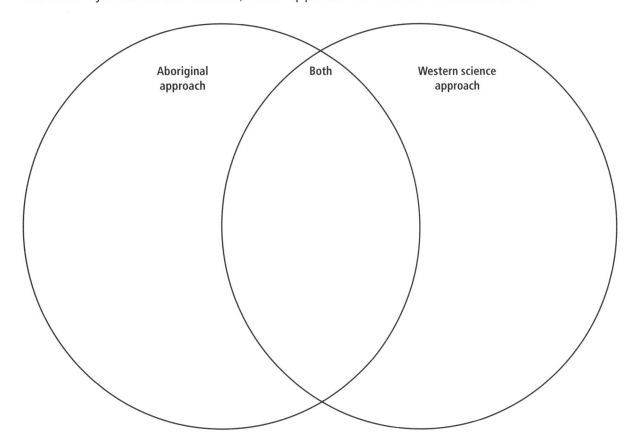

Use with textbook pages 426–429.

An interconnected universe

In an interconnected universe, all life forms are interconnected and related to one another. This unity of all includes the sea world, land world, spirit world, and sky world.

1. Draw a diagram that shows the ideas behind the interconnected universe. Be sure to explain how the parts of your diagram are related to each other.

(a) Diagram

(b) Explanation

_____

_____

_____

_____

_____

Use with textbook pages 426–429.

Aboriginal knowledge of the solar system

Match each Term on the left with the best Descriptor on the right. Each Descriptor may be used only once.	
Term	**Descriptor**
1. _____ realm 2. _____ holistic 3. _____ lunar month 4. _____ physical realm 5. _____ western science	**A.** the study of phenomena that can be physically observed, measured, documented, and tested **B.** studied in Western science **C.** an area such as the sea world, the land world, the spirit world, or the sky world **D.** a measurement of time from one new moon (or one full moon) to the next **E.** approach where all aspects of the physical and spiritual universe are connected to form a whole **F.** a study of the stars

Circle the letter of the best answer.

6. A holistic approach means to study

   A. only the physical universe

   B. only the spiritual universe

   C. all aspects of the solar system

   D. all aspects of the physical and spiritual universe

7. In the interconnected universe, Aboriginal peoples know that the realms

   A. are separate

   B. cannot be separated

   C. are loosely linked

   D. are independent

8. Aboriginal peoples developed a means of tracking and forecasting time based on

   A. tides

   B. charts

   C. the Moon

   D. Earth's rotation

9. The Coast Salish traditionally use a lunar cycle that is how many months long?

   A. six

   B. ten

   C. twelve

   D. thirteen

10. Observations of constellation movements have led to the body of knowledge known as

    A. geology

    B. astronomy

    C. geography

    D. physical science

11. Aboriginal peoples have long used their knowledge of the Moon's influence on

I.	fish species
II.	the weather
III.	ocean tides

    A. I and II only

    B. II and III only

    C. I and III only

    D. I, II, and III

Exploring Space: Past, Present, and Future

Textbook pages 432–449

Before You Read

Exploring and learning about space costs billions of dollars each year. Should we be spending so much money on space when there are still problems to solve here on Earth? Record your thoughts on the lines below.

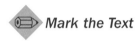

Mark the Text

Identify Definitions

As you read this section, highlight the definition of each word that appears in bold type.

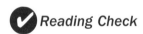

Reading Check

1. Which space technology would you use to collect data on the surface of the Moon?

What technologies help us observe and explore space?

The universe is so large and distances are so vast that it will be many years—if ever—before we can view much of it directly. Even here, in our solar system, the only object beyond Earth that humans have ever set foot on is the Moon. Most of what we know of the solar system and the rest of the universe depends on indirect observation using a variety of technologies like the following.

Optical telescopes: devices that collect and focus visible light from distant objects.

Radio telescopes: devices that collect and focus radio waves from distant objects and convert these waves into other forms so we can visualize them.

Satellites: electronic devices put in orbit around Earth to collect and send data back to Earth. Some satellites are used in communications services. If a satellite is stationary above a fixed point on Earth, it is in a **geosynchronous orbit**.

Probes: space vehicles that are sent to other planets and space objects to fly past, orbit, or land on them. Space probes are usually designed to travel very great distances and carry instruments to collect and relay large amounts of data.

Rovers: robotic devices that are designed to move around on the surface of a planet or moon, collecting visual and other types of data. ✔

What are the rewards and risks of space travel?

Space travel is made possible by rockets—devices that transport materials and equipment (and sometimes human explorers) into space. Some of the many rewards related to space travel and its associated technologies are freeze-dried foods, cold-weather clothing, global positioning systems (GPS), and bicycle helmets. Risks include the possibility of equipment failure (and possible injury or death), hazards of pollution in orbit around Earth, and hazards associated with this pollution when it falls back to Earth. ✅

✅ *Reading Check*

2. Name one benefit and one risk of space travel.

_____

_____

_____

Should we be travelling into space?

This is an ethical question. **Ethics** considers questions about whether something is right or wrong. Another ethical question is "Should we be **terraforming** other planets or moons—making them suitable for supporting human life?" Answering ethical questions often involves strong opinions and debate. There are many types of questions that need to be considered about space travel, including the following ones about space resources.

Questions about using space resources	
Ethical	• How can we ensure that space resources will be used to help all people? • Do humans have the right to take resources from other parts of the solar system?
Environmental	• What are the effects of space travel on Earth's natural systems? • What effects does removing resources have on other planets, asteroids, and moons?
Political	• Who owns space resources? • Who should decide how space resources will be used?

Use with textbook pages 432–445.

Space exploration

Vocabulary	
direct	rewards
ethics	risks
geosynchronous	rockets
indirect	rovers
optical	satellites
probes	terraforming
radio	

Use the terms in the vocabulary box to fill in the blanks. Each term may be used more than once. You will not need to use every term.

1. Most of what we know of the solar system and the rest of the universe depends on _____ observation using a variety of technologies.

2. _____ telescopes collect and focus the visible light from distant objects.

3. _____ telescopes collect and focus radio waves from distant objects.

4. _____ are put in orbit around Earth to send and receive data from Earth. If one stays in a fixed spot above Earth, it is in a _____ orbit.

5. _____ are space vehicles that are sent to other planets and space objects to fly past, orbit, or land on them.

6. _____ are robotic devices that are designed to move around on the surface of a planet or moon, collecting visual and other types of data.

7. Space travel is made possible by _____, which are devices that transport materials and equipment (and sometimes human explorers) into space.

8. _____ associated with space travel include freeze-dried foods, cold-weather clothing, global positioning systems (GPS), and bicycle helmets.

9. _____ associated with space travel include possible injury or death and hazards of pollution.

10. _____ considers questions about whether something is right or wrong.

11. _____ other planets or moons means making them suitable for supporting human life.

Use with textbook pages 432–445.

Exploring questions about space

What are your ideas about space travel?

1. Choose a question for each of the three following areas. You can use questions from the chart on page 183 or think of your own question for each area.

2. Explain your thoughts and ideas about an answer to each question. Back up your opinions with facts.

Question	Your ideas
(a) Ethical	
(b) Environmental	
(c) Political	

Use with textbook pages 439–445.

Technology for exploring space

Imagine that you have been selected to design a new technology for exploring space. You can design a new kind of telescope, probe, rover, satellite, or other technology.

1. Draw or describe your technology below. Label the main parts.

2. Describe what your technology does and how it works.

_____

_____

_____

_____

Use with textbook pages 432–445.

Exploring space: past, present, and future

Match each Term on the left with the best Descriptor on the right. Each Descriptor may be used only once.	
Term	**Descriptor**
1. _____ ethics	**A.** orbit is fixed above a spot on Earth
2. _____ geosynchronous	**B.** flies past, orbits, or lands on a celestial body to collect data
3. _____ optical telescope	**C.** electronic device put in orbit around Earth to relay information
4. _____ probe	**D.** considers whether something is right or wrong
5. _____ radio telescope	**E.** moves around and explores the surface of a planet
6. _____ rover	**F.** transforming a planet or moon into an Earth-like environment
7. _____ satellite	**G.** used to focus light from distant objects
8. _____ terraforming	**H.** collects radio waves and detects objects
	I. indirectly studies the solar system

Circle the letter of the best answer.

9. Which of the following is not a risk associated with space travel?

 A. possible injury and death

 B. pollution in space

 C. pollution on Earth

 D. high cost of developing technologies

10. Why does most of our knowledge of the solar system depend on indirect observation?

 A. There has not yet been enough study of the solar system.

 B. There are no tools for studying the solar system directly.

 C. Most of the solar system is too far away to study directly.

 D. It is too expensive to study the solar system directly.

11. Which of the following best describes rockets?

 A. devices that orbit in a fixed position above Earth

 B. devices that fly past other planets

 C. devices that collect data and relay them to Earth

 D. devices that transport materials, equipment, and human explorers into space

12. Which of the following is/are examples of ethical questions?

I.	How much money does it cost to send a probe to Mars?
II.	How can we control the probe once it is on Mars?
III.	Should we share the information we get from the probe on Mars?

 A. I only

 B. II only

 C. III only

 D. I, II, and III

Glossary

This Glossary provides the definitions of the key terms that are shown in boldface type in this workbook. The Glossary entries also show the sections where you can find the boldfaced words.

A

acetate a type of plastic used in photographic film and overhead transparencies (7.1)

alkali metals Group 1 metallic elements (lithium, sodium, potassium, rubidium, cesium, francium); all are strongly reactive, soft, and have low densities (2.2)

alkaline earth metals Group 2 metallic elements (beryllium, magnesium, calcium, strontium, barium, radium); all are reactive, fairly soft, and have fairly low densities (2.2)

ammeter a device used to measure the current in an electric circuit (8.2)

amperes (A) the unit for measuring electric current (8.2)

asteroid rocky material that orbits the Sun; most are found between Mars and Jupiter (11.2)

astronomers people who study objects in space (10.1)

atom the smallest particle of an element that still has the identity and properties of the element (1.3)

atomic number the number of protons in the nucleus of an atom of a given element (2.2)

average atomic mass the weighted average of the masses of the atoms of an element (2.2)

axis an imaginary line through Earth, extending from the North Pole to the South Pole (11.2)

axis tilt the tilt of Earth on its axis—an angle of 23.5° (12.1)

B

battery a device that stores electric potential energy so that it can be used at some later time to do work; made of electrochemical cells (8.1)

Big Bang theory the theory that proposes that the universe formed about 13.7 billion years ago when a very small, hot, and dense volume of space suddenly expanded and gave rise to all the energy and matter that now exists (10.1)

binary fission a form of asexual reproduction in which a single parent cell makes a copy of its genetic material and splits into two equal parts (5.2)

black hole a super-compact, super-dense object that forms when the core of a massive star collapses into itself (11.1)

blastula [BLAS-chuh-luh] a hollow ball of cells that forms after the second week of embryonic development (6.2)

Bohr model a diagram that shows the number of electrons in each energy level that surrounds the nucleus of an atom (2.3)

boiling point the temperature at which a substance changes state from a liquid to a gas (1.2)

budding a form of asexual reproduction in which a group of rapidly dividing cells develops on an organism and breaks away to become an identical organism, independent of its parent (5.2)

C

cancer a type of disease that results from uncontrolled cell division (5.1)

celestial bodies all the objects in space, including the Sun and other stars, the Moon, and planets (10.1)

cell cycle the three stages of the life of a cell (interphase, mitosis, and cytokinesis) (5.1)

charging by conduction the process of charging a neutral object by touching it to a charged object (7.2)

charging by induction the process of repelling or attracting electrons on a neutral object by bringing a charged object close to it (7.2)

chemical change a change in the chemical composition of a substance that results in the formation of one or more different substances (3.3)

chemical family elements in a group (vertical column) in the periodic table that have similar properties (e.g., alkali metals, alkaline earth metals, halogens, noble gases) (2.2)

chemical formula symbols that show the elements making up compounds and their ratios (3.2)

chemical name the name of a compound that indicates the elements in it (3.2)

chromosome a thread like structure consisting of a tightly packaged strand of DNA (4.1)

circuit diagram a picture made of symbols that represent the different parts of an electric circuit (8.2)

comet an object made of rock and ice that orbits the Sun in the outer limits of the solar system (11.2)

compound a pure substance that is made up of two or more elements that have been chemically combined (3.1)

conductivity a measure of how easily a material lets electricity or heat move through it (1.2)

conductors materials, such as metals, that allow electrons to move easily on and through them (7.1)

constellations distinctive groupings of stars; often look like familiar objects (12.1)

Copernicus, Nicolaus (1473–1543) Polish astronomer who, in the early 1500s, proposed a model of the heavens in which planets, including a rotating Earth, revolved around the Sun (12.1)

coulomb (C) the unit of electric charge; 1 C is the amount of charge passing a point in one second when one ampere of current is flowing (7.1)

covalent compounds compounds that form when atoms share electrons and form molecules (e.g., water) (3.1)

current electricity the continuous flow of charge through a conductor (8.2)

cytokinesis [SIH-toh-ki-NEE-sus] the last stage of the cell cycle in which the two equal and identical parts of the cell separate, resulting in two cells with the same DNA (5.1)

D

density the amount of mass in a certain volume of a substance or object (density equals mass divided by volume) (1.2)

differentiation the development of organs and body structures from blastula cell layers (6.2)

DNA a long, two-stranded molecule with a shape like a ladder that has been twisted into a spiral. DNA is found in the cell nucleus and stores the genetic material that carries the instructions for all the cell's life processes. Its genetic material is passed on from one generation to another when organisms reproduce. (4.1)

Doppler effect the change in the wavelengths of light or sound that occurs because the source is moving relative to the observer (11.1)

E

electric circuit a complete pathway through which electrons can flow (8.2)

electric current the amount of charge passing a point in a conducting wire each second (8.2)

electric force a pull (attraction) or a push (repulsion) between charged objects (7.2)

electric potential energy the energy stored in a battery that has the potential to make something move or change (8.1)

electrical power the rate at which electrical energy is changed into other forms of energy (9.2)

electrical resistance the property of a substance that slows down the movement of electrons and converts electrical energy into other forms of energy; in mathematical terms: $\text{resistance} = \dfrac{\text{voltage}}{\text{current}}$ (8.3)

electrochemical cell a device that converts chemical energy into electrical energy; also called a battery (8.1)

electrodes two terminals in a battery, usually made of metal (8.1)

electrolyte a substance that conducts electricity. In a dry cell, the electrolyte is a moist paste; in a wet cell, the electrolyte is an acidic solution. (8.1)

electron shells the energy levels around the nucleus of an atom in which electrons are located (2.3)

electrons negatively charged particles surrounding the atomic nucleus (1.3)

element a pure substance that cannot be broken down into other, simpler substances by chemical changes; all elements are listed on the periodic table (1.2)

elliptical galaxy one of three basic galaxy shapes; a galaxy that comes in a variety of shapes that range from a perfect sphere to a stretched-out sphere (10.2)

embryo [EM-bree-oh] the stage of a multicellular organism that develops from a zygote (6.1)

embryonic development the development that takes place during the first eight weeks after fertilization (6.2)

endothermic used to describe chemical reactions in which energy is absorbed (3.3)

energy the ability to do work (8.1)

ethics the set of moral principles and values that guides a person's actions and helps him or her decide what is right and what is wrong (12.3)

exothermic used to describe chemical reactions in which energy is released in the form of heat, light, sound, or other forms (3.3)

external fertilization fertilization in which a sperm cell and an egg cell join outside the bodies of the parents (6.2)

F

fertilization the process during which an egg cell is penetrated by a sperm cell (6.1)

fragmentation a form of asexual reproduction in which a small piece of an organism breaks away from the parent body and develops into an organism that is genetically identical to its parent (5.2)

fusion the process in which the nuclei of atoms fuse together to form larger single atoms, releasing tremendous amounts of energy (11.1)

G

Galileo Italian astronomer who confirmed Copernicus' model of a Sun-centred solar system (12.1)

gametes female organisms' and male organisms' specialized cells necessary for reproduction (6.1)

gene a small segment of DNA that carries instructions for making proteins (4.1)

gene mutation a change in the genetic material (DNA) of a gene (4.2)

gene therapy new techniques for treating gene mutations (4.2)

geosynchronous orbit the orbit of a satellite that remains above a fixed point on Earth (12.3)

grounding allowing electric charge to flow into Earth's surface (7.1)

H

halogens Group 17 non-metallic elements that are strongly reactive and are gases at room temperature (except for bromine, which is a liquid) (2.2)

holistic a view that sees all aspects of the physical and spiritual universe as connected to form a whole (12.2)

homologous chromosomes a pair of matching chromosomes (6.1)

I

insulators materials, such as plastic, rubber, wool, and glass, that do not allow electrons to move on or through them easily (7.1)

internal fertilization fertilization in which a sperm cell joins an egg cell inside the female's body (6.2)

interphase the first stage of the cell cycle in which cells grow, carry out life functions, and the nuclei of the cells that will divide make copies of their DNA (5.1)

ionic compounds compounds that form when atoms gain electrons from other atoms or lose electrons to other atoms, resulting in ions of opposite charge that attract each other (3.1)

ionic lattice the repeating pattern of positive and negative ions in an ionic compound (3.1)

irregular galaxy one of the three basic galaxy shapes; a galaxy that is not shaped like a sphere or a pinwheel (10.2)

J

joule (J) the unit for measuring energy (9.2)

junction point the place where pathways separate or join in a parallel circuit (9.1)

K

Kepler, Johannes (1571–1630) German mathematician who, in the early 1600s, predicted that the planets revolved around the Sun in elliptical orbits, not circles as was thought (12.1)

kilowatt-hour (kW·h) a product of power, in kilowatts, and time, in hours; is the same amount of energy as 1000 W over a period of 1 h (9.2)

L

laws of static charge physical laws that describe interactions between charged and uncharged objects; that is, like charges repel, opposite charges attract, and charged objects attract neutral objects (7.2)

light-year the distance that light travels in one year (11.3)

lunar eclipse an event in which the Earth passes between the Sun and the Moon, plunging the Moon into darkness (12.1)

lunar month the length of time from one new moon (or one full moon) to the next; equal to about 29.5 days (12.2)

M

mass the amount of matter in a substance or an object (1.2)

mating the means by which gametes (sperm and egg cells) meet in the same place at the same time (6.2)

meiosis [mih-OH-sus] the process that produces gametes with half the number of chromosomes as body cells (6.1)

melting point the temperature at which a substance changes state from a solid to a liquid (1.2)

metalloids elements that have some properties that are like metals and others that are like non-metals. Metalloids form a zigzag staircase shape near the right side of the periodic table. (2.2)

metals elements that typically have the following physical properties: solids at room temperature (except for mercury, which is a liquid), shiny, malleable, ductile, and good conductors of heat and electricity (2.1)

mitosis [mih-TOH-sus] the second stage of the cell cycle in which the nucleus divides into two equal and identical parts that each have one copy of the DNA (5.1)

molecule a neutral particle consisting of atoms that are joined together by the sharing of electrons (3.1)

moon an object that orbits a planet (11.2)

multiple ion charge a characteristic of elements whose atoms can gain or lose electrons in more than one way (2.2)

multivalent metals metals that can form two or more different positive ions with different charges (3.2)

mutagens substances or factors that can cause mutations in DNA (4.2)

N

nebula a dense, cloud-like collection of gas and dust in space (10.2)

negative mutation a mutation that harms an organism (4. 2)

neutral mutation a mutation that neither harms nor helps an organism (4.2)

neutron an uncharged particle in the atomic nucleus (1.3)

noble gases Group 18 non-metallic elements that are normally unreactive and are colourless, odourless gases at room temperature (2.2)

non-metals elements that typically have the following physical properties: gases or brittle solids at room temperature (except for bromine, which is a liquid), not shiny, not malleable, not ductile, and not good conductors of heat and electricity (2.1)

nucleolus a membrane-free organelle that floats in the interior of the nucleus and makes ribosomes (4.1)

nucleus in chemistry, the positively charged core of an atom, which contains protons and neutrons (1.3); in biology, an organelle that directs and controls all of the cell's activities (4.1)

O

ohm (Ω) the unit used for measuring electrical resistance (8.3)

Ohm's law a mathematical equation that shows how voltage (V), current (I), and resistance (R) are related: $R = \frac{V}{I}$ (8.3)

optical telescope a device that collects and focuses the visible light from distant objects (12.3)

P

parallax the apparent change in position of a nearby object when it is viewed from two different points (11.3)

parallel circuit an electric circuit that has two or more pathways for electric current to take (9.1)

periodic table a table that organizes each element into a single box based on its chemical and physical properties. Each box may include the name of the element, the chemical symbol of the element, the atomic number, the average atomic mass, and the ion charge(s). (2.2)

physical change a change in the appearance of a substance that does not result in a change in its chemical composition, and in which no new substances are formed (3.3)

planet a spherical object made mainly of rock or gases, which orbits a star and is large enough that its own gravity holds it in a spherical shape (11.2)

polyatomic ion an ion consisting of two or more atoms that are held together by covalent bonds (3.1)

positive mutation a mutation that is helpful to an organism (4.2)

potential difference the difference in the amount of electrical potential energy per coulomb of charge between two points in a electric circuit; also called voltage (8.1)

power the rate of change in energy (9.2)

power rating a measurement of how many joules of energy a device uses each second of operation (9.2)

probe a space vehicle that carries scientific instruments and flies past, orbits, or lands on a celestial body to collect data (12.3)

proteins molecules that all cells of the body need in order to work properly (4.1)

protons positively charged subatomic particles (1.3)

Ptolemy Greek astronomer who thought that Earth was at the centre of the universe (12.1)

R

radiation energy that is transmitted in the form of waves and can be picked up from every part of space (10.1)

radio telescope a device that collects and focuses radio waves from distant objects and converts this radiation into other forms so we can visualize them (12.3)

red shift the shifting of an object's light towards the red (longer wavelength) end of the spectrum as the object moves away from Earth (10.1)

replication the process during which the nucleus of a cell makes a copy of its DNA (5.1)

resistor a component in an electric circuit with a specific resistance that slows down current and transforms electrical energy into other forms of energy (8.3)

revolution the motion of a planet as it travels around the Sun (11.2)

ribosome an organelle without a membrane that produces proteins (4.1)

Roman numerals numerals based on those used by the ancient Romans (3.2)

rotation the motion of a planet as it spins on its axis (11.2)

rover a robotic device that is designed to move around on the surface of a planet or moon, collecting visual and other types of data (12.3)

S
satellites electronic devices put into orbit around Earth to collect and send data back to Earth (12.3)

series circuit an electric circuit that has only one path for electric current to take (9.1)

sexual reproduction means of passing genetic information from two parent cells to an offspring (6.1)

solar system a group of planets circling a star (11.2)

spectroscope an instrument that can separate white light into its component wavelengths of colour (10.1)

spindle fibres tiny tube-like structures made of protein to which chromosomes attach during mitosis (5.1)

spiral galaxy one of the three basic galaxy shapes; a galaxy that looks like a pinwheel (10.2)

spores single cells that can develop into new individuals by repeated mitosis (5.2)

star a massive, gaseous, spherical object in space that gives off light and other forms of energy due to nuclear reactions that take place at its core (11.1)

star clusters distinct groups of stars that are found within galaxies; the two main types are globular clusters, which are larger and held together by gravity in a spherical shape, and open clusters, which are smaller and contain stars of roughly the same age (10.2)

state a property of matter; may be solid, liquid, or gas (1.2)

static charge an electric charge that can build up and stay very nearly fixed in one place for some length of time (7.1)

stem cells cells that can divide to become one of many different types of cells (5.2)

subatomic particles particles that are smaller than atoms. These particles include protons, neutrons, and electrons. (1.3)

supernova a dramatic, powerful explosion that occurs when a high mass star collapses in on itself (11.1)

T

terraforming the act of making planets (other than Earth) or moons more suitable for supporting human life (12.3)

triangulation a technique for determining the distance to a visible object by creating an imaginary triangle between the observer and the object and then calculating the distance (11.3)

V

valence electrons electrons in the outermost electron shell—the valence shell (2.3)

valence shell the electron shell that holds the electrons that are farthest away from the nucleus of an atom (2.3)

Van de Graaff generator a machine that uses friction to produce a build-up of static charge (7.1)

vegetative reproduction a form of asexual reproduction in which special cells, usually in the stems and roots of plants, divide repeatedly to form structures that develop into a plant that is identical to the parent (5.2)

volt (V) the standard unit for voltage (or potential difference) (8.1)

voltage the difference in the amount of electrical potential energy per coulomb of charge at one point in a electric circuit and another point in the circuit; also called potential difference (8.1)

voltmeter a device that measures the amount of potential difference between two points in an electric circuit (8.1)

volume the amount of space that a substance or object takes up (1.2)

W

watt (W) one joule per second (9.2)

Western science science that is based mainly on the physical realm (12.2)

Workplace Hazardous Materials Information System (WHMIS) a system that uses eight safety symbols to provide safety information about materials and products (1.1)

Z

zygote [ZIH-guht] the new cell that results when an egg cell and a sperm cell join (fertilization); the first body cell of the new organism (6.1)

Notes

Periodic Table of the Elements

Legend:
- metal
- metalloid (outlined)
- non-metal

Example box:
22 — Atomic number
Ti — Symbol
Titanium — Name
47.9 — Average atomic mass**
4+, 3+ — Ion charge(s)

- O — natural
- Db — synthetic

Group 1

| 1 H Hydrogen 1.0 (1+) |
| 3 Li Lithium 6.9 (1+) |
| 11 Na Sodium 23.0 (1+) |
| 19 K Potassium 39.1 (1+) |
| 37 Rb Rubidium 85.5 (1+) |
| 55 Cs Cesium 132.9 (1+) |
| 87 Fr Francium (223) (1+) |

Group 2

| 4 Be Beryllium 9.0 (2+) |
| 12 Mg Magnesium 24.3 (2+) |
| 20 Ca Calcium 40.1 (2+) |
| 38 Sr Strontium 87.6 (2+) |
| 56 Ba Barium 137.3 (2+) |
| 88 Ra Radium (226) (2+) |

Transition metals (Groups 3–12)

Period 4:
- 21 Sc Scandium 45.0 (3+)
- 22 Ti Titanium 47.9 (4+, 3+)
- 23 V Vanadium 50.9 (5+, 4+)
- 24 Cr Chromium 52.0 (3+, 2+)
- 25 Mn Manganese 54.9 (2+, 4+)
- 26 Fe Iron 55.8 (3+, 2+)
- 27 Co Cobalt 58.9 (2+, 3+)
- 28 Ni Nickel 58.7 (2+, 3+)
- 29 Cu Copper 63.5 (2+, 1+)
- 30 Zn Zinc 65.4 (2+)

Period 5:
- 39 Y Yttrium 88.9 (3+)
- 40 Zr Zirconium 91.2 (4+)
- 41 Nb Niobium 92.9 (3+, 5+)
- 42 Mo Molybdenum 95.9 (3+, 6+)
- 43 Tc Technetium (98) (7+)
- 44 Ru Ruthenium 101.1 (3+, 4+)
- 45 Rh Rhodium 102.9 (3+)
- 46 Pd Palladium 106.4 (2+, 4+)
- 47 Ag Silver 107.9 (1+)
- 48 Cd Cadmium 112.4 (2+)

Period 6:
- 57 La Lanthanum 138.9 (3+)
- 72 Hf Hafnium 178.5 (4+)
- 73 Ta Tantalum 180.9 (5+)
- 74 W Tungsten 183.8 (6+)
- 75 Re Rhenium 186.2 (4+, 7+)
- 76 Os Osmium 190.2 (3+, 4+)
- 77 Ir Iridium 192.2 (3+, 4+)
- 78 Pt Platinum 195.1 (4+, 2+)
- 79 Au Gold 197.0 (3+, 1+)
- 80 Hg Mercury 200.6 (2+, 1+)

Period 7:
- 89 Ac Actinium (227) (3+)
- 104 Rf Rutherfordium (261)
- 105 Db Dubnium (262)
- 106 Sg Seaborgium (263)
- 107 Bh Bohrium (262)
- 108 Hs Hassium (265)
- 109 Mt Meitnerium (266)
- 110 Ds Darmstadtium (281)
- 111 Rg Roentgenium (272)
- 112 Uub* Ununbium (285)

Groups 13–18

- 5 B Boron 10.8 (3+)
- 6 C Carbon 12.0 (4+)
- 7 N Nitrogen 14.0 (3+, 3-)
- 8 O Oxygen 16.0 (2-)
- 9 F Fluorine 19.0 (1-)
- 2 He Helium 4.0 (0)
- 10 Ne Neon 20.2 (0)

- 13 Al Aluminum 27.0 (3+)
- 14 Si Silicon 28.1 (4+)
- 15 P Phosphorus 31.0 (3-)
- 16 S Sulphur 32.1 (2-)
- 17 Cl Chlorine 35.5 (1-)
- 18 Ar Argon 39.9 (0)

- 31 Ga Gallium 69.7 (3+)
- 32 Ge Germanium 72.6 (4+, 2+)
- 33 As Arsenic 74.9 (3-)
- 34 Se Selenium 79.0 (2-)
- 35 Br Bromine 79.9 (1-)
- 36 Kr Krypton 83.8 (0)

- 49 In Indium 114.8 (3+)
- 50 Sn Tin 118.7 (4+, 2+)
- 51 Sb Antimony 121.8 (3+, 5+)
- 52 Te Tellurium 127.6 (2-)
- 53 I Iodine 126.9 (1-)
- 54 Xe Xenon 131.3 (0)

- 81 Tl Thallium 204.4 (1+, 3+)
- 82 Pb Lead 207.2 (2+, 4+)
- 83 Bi Bismuth 209.0 (3+, 5+)
- 84 Po Polonium (209) (2+, 4+)
- 85 At Astatine (210) (1-)
- 86 Rn Radon (222) (0)

- 113 Uut* Ununtrium (284)
- 114 Uuq* Ununquadium (289)
- 115 Uup* Ununpentium (288)
- 116 Uuh* Ununhexium (292)

* Temporary names

Lanthanides (period 6):

- 58 Ce Cerium 140.1 (3+, 4+)
- 59 Pr Praseodymium 140.9 (3+, 4+)
- 60 Nd Neodymium 144.2 (3+)
- 61 Pm Promethium (145) (3+)
- 62 Sm Samarium 150.4 (3+, 2+)
- 63 Eu Europium 152.0 (3+, 2+)
- 64 Gd Gadolinium 157.3 (3+)
- 65 Tb Terbium 158.9 (3+, 4+)
- 66 Dy Dysprosium 162.5 (3+)
- 67 Ho Holmium 164.9 (3+)
- 68 Er Erbium 167.3 (3+)
- 69 Tm Thulium 168.9 (3+, 2+)
- 70 Yb Ytterbium 173.0 (3+, 2+)
- 71 Lu Lutetium 175.0 (3+)

Actinides (period 7):

- 90 Th Thorium 232.0 (4+)
- 91 Pa Protactinium 231.0 (5+, 4+)
- 92 U Uranium 238.0 (6+, 4+, 5+)
- 93 Np Neptunium (237) (5+, 4+, 6+)
- 94 Pu Plutonium (244) (5+, 6+, 3+, 4+)
- 95 Am Americium (243) (3+, 4+, 5+, 6+)
- 96 Cm Curium (247) (3+)
- 97 Bk Berkelium (247) (3+, 4+)
- 98 Cf Californium (251) (3+, 4+)
- 99 Es Einsteinium (252) (3+)
- 100 Fm Fermium (257) (3+)
- 101 Md Mendelevium (258) (2+, 3+)
- 102 No Nobelium (259) (2+, 3+)
- 103 Lr Lawrencium (262) (3+)

**Based on mass of carbon-12 at 12.00 u.

Any value in parentheses is the mass of the most stable or best known isotope for elements that do not occur naturally.